MAN AND THE SUN

JACQUETTA HAWKES

MAN
AND
THE SUN

LONDON: THE CRESSET PRESS 1962

© 1962 by Jacquetta Hawkes
Published in Great Britain by
The Cresset Press, 11 Fitzroy Square, London, W.1
First published 1962

Printed in Great Britain by
Western Printing Services Ltd., Bristol

TO

JOHN AND MARGHANITA HOWARD

Acknowledgments

I should like to thank Professor Hoyle of Cambridge for permission to use the Sun Formula and his comments (pp. 245-6), Dr Strehlow of Adelaide for the quotation from his *Aranda Traditions* (pp. 51-2) and Mr Laurens van der Post for calling my attention to the Bushman story (p. 53). I am also much indebted to Mr John Sinclair, curator of the Coronado Monument, New Mexico, and his assistant Valencio, for information about the sun in Pueblo religion.

Contents

List of Plates

Figures in the Text

In the centre of everything is the Sun. Nor could anyone have placed this luminary at any other, better point in this beautiful temple, than that from which it can illuminate everything uniformly. Not without grounds, therefore, do some call it the World's Lamp, others—Reason—still others—the Ruler, Trismehist— the Visible Deity, Sophocles' Electra—the All-Seeing. Thus, the Sun is pictured seated on his throne, ruling over the family of stars around him.

COPERNICUS

BIRTH OF THE SUN

THE YELLOW-HAMMER IS the first. His little stutter followed after a pause by the single note, pure, sustained but rather too shrill, make the first mark upon the grey silence of earliest morning. He repeats himself again and again, the thin song seems to waver horizontally through the air, thin and uninspiring. But it is enough to rouse the rest. Scores of hard, round eyes are unlidded, feathers shaken and puffed up. The blackbirds, the thrushes and missel-thrushes, several species of warbler with songs more various than their plumage, all come in together. But unlike the yellow-hammers, their singing seems to spout upward and fall in full, clear drops.

Roused by the dawn chorus, some human being in the house on the hill lifts the corner of a curtain. The sky is growing lighter and the stars more dim, although Jupiter is still flashing above the western horizon. At this moment sky and grass seem to reflect one another, for lawns and fields are faintly silvered with dew—milliards of grains of water which the sun yesterday lifted into the air, and which in its absence the air has let fall again.

In absolute tranquillity the earth spins round its axis at some thousand miles an hour, and round the sun at eleven hundred miles a minute; earth, the Morning Star and the still invisible sun are wheeling round their galactic hub at half a million miles

B   I

an hour. Not a leaf nor a blade stirs. Only the bird notes disturb
the hush attending sunrise.

The earth spins with one plump hemisphere for ever held in
sunlight, the other in shadow, where the cone of darkness
stands above it like a tent. And now as some part of farthest
Asia enters this tent of night, here southern England turns into
the sunlight. Twenty minutes later Ireland follows it, and then
the great watery convexity of the Atlantic begins to lift out of
darkness so that four hours later the sun's beams will be striking
upon Cape Cod.

This would be the view of an observing god, and to this
same distant eye and ear it would appear that a continuous dawn
chorus rose from one segment of the globe, interrupted only
when oceans or birdless lands were passing through it. And this
choral zone would lie between the illumined hemisphere of
perpetual activity and noise and the darkened hemisphere
always quieter and more stealthy.

But for the human being in the house on the hill this external
vision of the planet is unreal, only to be attained after strenuous
wrestling with the imagination. All the aeons of evolutionary
experience, the seemingly endless chain of days and nights since
life began, have helped to condition man into believing his own
eyes, into knowing that the sun rises, swings across the vault
and drops into the west. It was the view the Egyptians took
when they saw the sun god Re sailing the heavens in a boat; it
was the view of the Greeks when they saw Apollo driving his
chariot; it was the view of the Aztecs when they saw themselves as children of the sun, of Huitzilopochtli, helping him to
fight the moon and stars and put darkness to flight. In despite
of Copernican knowledge it is ours today—and there is a sense
in which our terrestrial point of view is no less justified than any
other.

As the sun rises, the thin skin of life between the earth's rocky
crust and its enclosing atmosphere responds, each species after
its fashion. Flowers open; reptiles gain the warmth that enables

2

them to move; many animals set out on their quest for food while a few others retire to sleep; most human beings wake up and put on their clothes; green leaves renew their daily task of turning carbon dioxide into oxygen. The variety of living forms dependent more or less directly on the sun's radiation is enormous. The species of plants and creatures living in the air and water and on land run into hundreds of millions; the range of their shapes and colours and modes of wresting a living from their environment makes the wonder of creation. And within these myriads of living bodies is further complexity—all the regiments of physiology, the innumerable different types of organ and cell and other microscopic agents of life. Although the species progress in size from the virus to the elephant, giraffe and whale, and from the single-celled plant to the giant sequoia, all alike are as grains of dust in relation to their lord the sun. Yes, these living things are small, varied and complex, while the star on which they depend is relatively huge and simple. Yet life and star, so utterly unlike one another, are built from the same bricks, and were once, it seems, part of the same almost uniform mass.

The strangest element in this difference and in this relationship has not been mentioned. It is consciousness. With mind's new understanding of the unity of the cosmos, it must recognize itself as being in some sense present in the rocks and minerals; even in the furnace of the sun. One would like to be able to comprehend in what manner it is present in inorganic matter. But it remains beyond our comprehension. We can only appeal to the time dimension, saying that it must always have been present in matter because in the course of some thousands of millions of years it emerged from it. In fact that consciousness is there rather as a butterfly is present in the minute globlet laid upon the leaf, and a man or woman in the fertilized human ovum. Surely a full historical understanding of the universe would enable us to see the emergence of consciousness to be as inevitable as that of the butterfly or human being?

3

Once we pass from inorganic to living matter the hierarchy of consciousness is easily imaginable. We can be aware of it in plants (perhaps best expressed in sensitively groping tendrils), and certainly, though cold and remote, in fish and reptiles; in insects and more especially in birds it is evidently intense, however alien from our own. Perhaps the birds, so brilliant and aesthetically gifted, are inaccessible to us because so far removed in evolutionary origins. Certainly we can approach ourselves with more sympathetic understanding through the mammals with whom we share so many of the basic experiences of life. Indeed with our nearest mammalian kin, the great apes, we always feel a little awkward. The difference between us seems so slight, that the contrast between our domination of the earth and the apes' bare survival in a few patches of undesirable jungle strikes us as embarrassing. We stand before the chimpanzee's cage thinking, each one of us, there but for the grace of God swing I. Of recent years, it is true, we have been less confident that the comparison is to our advantage.

Here, then, we have the degrees of consciousness rising from inorganic matter to the mind of man, where it reaches its greatest intensity within our solar system. It expresses one aspect of the intense relationship between all parts of that system and particularly between sun, terrestrial life and mankind. The sun provided most of the matter of the earth, and not only holds it on its orbit, saving it from dashing off to destruction or meaningless wandering through space, but has quickened it to life and maintained this life while it evolved. Then, as in the light of its rays, mind flowered in man, our kind looked up at the sun, were intuitively aware of its creative might and their utter dependence upon it and saw it to be bright with divinity. In many different manners they worshipped the Sun God and knew the mystic union which in very historic truth bound them together. But as their rational capacity grew and their intuition weakened, men deprived the sun of the divinity which they had given it, and instead of worshipping it they anatomized it, discovering its size and weight and distance away, what stuff it was made of, how it burned and moved. They speculated as to its past history and future prospects. Finally we have begun to imitate it, to make little suns of our own, and at this point we are threatened with self-destruction like Icarus, like Prometheus and all such brave, dangerous and presumptuous trespassers.

This great and most curious cycle is the subject of my book. I shall begin with what in fact happened first as an historical event in finite time, even although all mental apprehension of it belongs to the very end of my cycle. I shall begin, that is to say, with the birth of the sun and its planets. It must be admitted at once that just because these events are among the last to have been brought within the grasp of rational thought, they are still the most uncertain. Indeed, as a tyro in these matters I was severely shocked when I compared what that penetrating student of the universe, Fred Hoyle, had said on the subject in 1950 with his quite different account of five years later. Prehistory has accustomed me to the idea of playing with the facts of the human past, but to juggle with a star and nine planets shows far greater temerity. I write these descriptions, then, knowing that before long the ancient events to which they refer will have been changed: changed in the only place where they have been given mental shape—in the minds of men. This does not worry me, for while on the one hand the exact nature of these events cannot affect my true theme, on the other the meaning lying behind them will remain inscrutable however they come to be ordered by the scientists. Scientific reconstructions are fascinating; they make it possible to envisage the movements of the great cosmic dance, but they must always reach an ultimate point of mystery where they become finally irrelevant. For the Egyptians the cosmos was created by the Sun God Atum from a hillock of slime among primordial waters. For the astro-physicists it is either exploding from a primordial mass or eternally renewing itself from hydrogen

5

atoms. When we reach the final question of them all, the answer of the scientists is no more significant than that of the myth-makers.

There is one thing I should dearly like to know and which may some day be knowable. In all this vast scheme of things, among all glittering realms of the galaxies whirling through space, are there many other globes besides our own where matter has focused into mind and mind is striving to apprehend the universe?

Playing with noughts is a meaningless game for anyone except the mathematician. But if the formation of planetary systems is frequent among the starry hosts, if indeed there are 100,000 million in our Milky Way alone, then it is overwhelmingly probable that there are innumerable points of consciousness comparable to our earthly one, where beings, or perhaps sometimes a single integrated being, are mentally probing the universe about them, mapping, calculating, speculating as diligently as we ourselves. If they are, then is it not likely that these planetary points of consciousness will at some future time come into communication one with another even as individual men are now learning to communicate over the entire surface of the earth? And if there were such cosmic mental intercourse, might not the whole be likened to the human brain where 13,000 million cells all work in unison in the service of consciousness, 'a sparkling field of rhythmic flashing points with trains of travelling sparks hurrying hither and thither'? Perhaps aeons hence some such universal brain will have apprehensions as much greater than our own as ours are greater than the apprehension of the amoeba or the rocks.

I should like to know these things, but cannot. Perhaps I have been born too soon; perhaps they will never be known to us. As it is I must be content to tell the tale as it is being written here on this particular planet.

At this moment I am sitting at my desk smoking a cigarette, and the beams despatched by the hero of my story are striking

6

through the window at my side. The air is quite still, and the smoke curls slowly upward through the sunlight forming heavy coils, fluffy masses and light, drifting wisps. Four thousand million years ago a cloud which from afar off would have looked very much the same, coiled on the periphery of a glittering disk of stars. This cloud, however, was composed of hydrogen gas mingled with a lesser amount of dust, probably carbon particles derived from the burning stars of the central disk. For these stars at the hub of our galaxy had already been in existence for some thousand million years. Moreover, they had formed in ways rather different from those now coming into being in the spiral arms projecting from the hub exactly as the sails project from a paper windmill.

My tobacco smoke towers up towards the ceiling, and after some noble coiling and wreathing dissipates itself and becomes invisible. The cloud of interstellar gas, on the contrary, was vast enough to condense through the forces of gravity. The hydrogen atoms and the carbon grains pulled together, growing hotter even as they became more compact. Then, as the heat rose to 3,000 degrees, a dramatic fission began within the condensing cloud. It broke into smaller clouds, and each fragment as it shrank and heated divided yet again. Soon they ceased to be smokelike, having formed dense masses made opaque by dust and therefore showing like dark clots against the glowing galactial lights. At last further fragmentation ceased, and the core of each clot compacted into a glowing, spinning ball of gas. Hanging in space among the remnants of the clouds, the newborn stars clustered together like a rocket shower with its points of fire gleaming among the drifting smoke.

This great transformation scene from cloud into stars lasted only a few thousand years, a mere instant on the cosmic time scale. Similar events continue here in the spiral arms of our galaxy whenever large enough clouds are swept together. Anyone who wishes to see a cluster even now coming into shining life should turn a telescope upon the faint smudge of light just

7

visible to the unaided eye by the sword of Orion—surely the most commanding constellation in all our northern heavens. In this Orion nebula, a glowing gas cloud about 100,000,000,000,000 miles across, new stars are continually forming. To see a cluster already created but quite young, and therefore not yet dispersed as most clusters are dispersed by the gravitational drags of the galaxy, the telescope should be turned to the group of bright stars of which Persei is one. These stars were born only a million years ago, so that although they are rushing away from one another at twelve kilometres a second they still form a coherent astral cloud. The Pleiades or Seven Sisters, that intimate little constellation which in truth possesses in Plione a star a thousand times brighter than the sun, is a visible example of an open cluster, one which for reasons of its own has expanded some little way from its original compactness, but remains knit in a loose community.

Returning now to 4,000 million years ago and the birth of the cluster which is of such dear significance to ourselves, we can see that the members of this astral family range in size from some rather smaller than the future sun to a few many times as large. One among these outside stars merits our most sympathetic interest, for it was destined to destroy itself and in so doing to yield much of the substance of terrestrial life. Out of the stupendous furnace at its heart were to come the atomic bricks from which our familiar surroundings, our yet more familiar possessions, were to be made. From its heart, too, were to come the carbon, nitrogen and oxygen of our own bodies, the dwelling-place and very being of our most precious Selves.

All stars, wherever they occur, with cores considerably more massive than the sun are condemned from birth to relatively rapid self-destruction. In recent times the power of human thought here on earth has provided the explanation of these vast stellar catastrophes. Whether at the time of the particular catastrophe we are about to describe there was any comparable planetary intelligence to observe or interpret it we are never

8

likely to be certain. But judging from the age of the galaxy, only 1,000 million years old when this event took place, and from the fact that it has taken some three or four times as long as that for an analytical intelligence to evolve on earth, the chances seem very much against it. Probably the giant star to which we owe so much condensed, burned, collapsed and exploded unseen and unrecorded. The creation of its historians lay far in the future.

The incandescent ball spun among hundreds of thousands of smaller siblings. The parental gas cloud had been large enough to bring it three or four times the number of hydrogen particles which were to go into our sun. So great a mass caused an unimaginable gravitational thrust, with resulting fiercer heat and more crushing density. Because of this stupendous thrust and other much subtler chemical and nuclear reactions, this giant star could not establish the constantly adjusting pressure balances which, as we shall see, will give the sun and its equally moderate companions a long life and relatively peaceful death. This *supernova* could not cool down, but had to pour out more and more radiation, stoke up more and more energy at its heart in order to do so. It became a vast nuclear furnace splitting the nuclei of atoms and building up new heavier and more complex elements. The dance of the protons and neutrons became faster and more ornate, with ever more elaborate figures and new partnerships. In time the original hydrogen remained only as an outer skin, and inwards from it, ever hotter and more dense, went layer after layer of the new elements from helium, carbon, oxygen and neon in and in through magnesium and silicon to a metallic core with iron, cobalt, nickel, copper, zinc, chromium, manganese and many other massive substances fated to fall into human hands.

This moment in the life of the *supernova* was a crucial one, its rapid and most violent end already prefigured. The pressure in the metallic heart was now 100,000,000,000,000,000 pounds upon every square inch, the temperature over 2,000 million degrees and the density such that a matchbox full of the matter would be too heavy for our strongest cranes to lift.

While hitherto evolutionary changes in the star had taken many millions of years, now they accelerated towards their catastrophic climax. As the inmost temperature rose to 3,000 million degrees the dreadful shrinkage was conspicuous in the trifling span of a terrestrial year, and at 4,000 within a month. Then at 5,000 million degrees the crisis came. First another wild dance and shuffling of the protons and neutrons caused the great central furnace to collapse; it had ceased to be able to make good the energy streaming out into space from the cooler but still blue-hot surface. A giant star which had burned in the firmament for hundreds of millions of years suffered this collapse in one second of time. Briefly it rallied, but as the mighty outer layers fell in upon the collapsed heart, an indescribable cataclysm which again took place in the space of seconds, overwhelming waves of heat rushed outwards and provoked so violent an increase in the nuclear reactions of the outer skins that they blew up in one of the greatest explosions the cosmos can ever know. Compared with this, the most powerful nuclear blast man in his madness has yet achieved is no more than the popping of a cap pistol is to the bomb itself.

As the huge ball was shattered, atoms of all the elements created within during its evolution tore outwards through space forming once again a huge cloud of gas, but a cloud which instead of condensing was now expanding from the force of the explosion at a rate of some 2,000 kilometres a second. A fragment of the bursting giant may perhaps have clung together and even now be burning somewhere in our heavens, a modest star no longer troubled by the dangers attending all forms of greatness.

Exploding *supernovae* in our galaxy have been observed during the span of historic times on earth. One in particular is remarkable because it was near enough to be seen with the naked eye in days before telescopes. In A.D. 1054 the learned and observant astronomers of China saw, and exactly recorded, a brilliant outburst in the sky in the neighbourhood of the constellation Taurus. It must have been equally dazzling a spectacle in Europe, but if anyone thought it worth noting down, his note has been lost. This celestial firework probably kept its inexpressible first brilliance for some weeks, then very gradually faded. Today it forms the Crab Nebula in Taurus, a many-armed patch of light which still, when photographed, seems to show the rough vigour of an explosion.

For me the Crab Nebula offers a good exercise for an imaginative grasp of the dimensions of time and space with which our universe confronts us. To try to picture not only our own galaxy, but all those others in its group, and then those many, many other groups of galaxies powdering the heavens like a snow shower, on and on until they fade out of our sight beyond the reach of the most powerful telescope, is something before which the imagination is bound to fail. The Crab Nebula is within our own galaxy; it is just imaginable. Look, then, at this apparently small mass of glowing gas and particles, and reflect that it represents a *supernova* which shattered twelve years before the Norman Conquest of Britain. Ever since that time its particles have been hastening outwards at the rate of 1,000 kilometres a second. Yet even now, after nine centuries, it is still relatively compact, its writhen arms and jagged, turbulent centre still retain the pattern of an explosion.

The *supernova* to which we on earth owe so much had, of course, passed far beyond the state of the Crab before its fate began to intertwine with our own. Its gases, the atoms of all the elements created in its furnace, were fully dispersed among the clouds of interstellar hydrogen in which star showers were still forming as before. The heavier elements, all those atoms of iron, copper, zinc and the rest, were indeed so thinly scattered through the cloud that they formed only about one hundredth part of weight of the hydrogen.

Still this cloud was condensing and fragmenting just as when the *supernova* itself was born, but now every shrinking fragment contained its share of heavy elements. And among them was one marked out to be known to man as *Sol Invictus*, the Unconquerable Sun.

At first this solar cloud was almost spherical, but as it shrank it also inevitably spun faster and faster and the rotary forces caused it to flatten more and more until it had assumed the shape of the squatter kinds of spinning-top. Then, when it had contracted about to the circumference now circled by the planet Mercury, and was already dense enough to be called a star, the speed of its gyrations caused a disk of its own substance to begin to project from its widest girth just as a rim of tin often projects from a top where the two halves have been united. As the spinning continued this disk extended further from the sun while the sun itself continued to shrink until a gap was drawn between the sun and a now wholly external disk. However, this wide halo of gas did not cease to spin, for it was still tied to the sun by the invisible bonds of a magnetic field. These served to keep it in motion very nearly as fast as the parental star, but at the same time it dragged upon the sun, holding it back and gradually reducing its speed. As the sun slowed towards its present rate of some two kilometres a second at the equator, the flattening naturally ceased and it rose up again towards its poles, becoming the almost perfect ball we have all seen through smoked glass or evening mists.

Meanwhile strange things were happening to the whirling disk of matter. For even as this vast equatorial halo was thrust further and further out, the zones nearer to the parent sun could have been observed to be clotting into chunks of solid matter. As the gas cooled it was inevitable that the atoms of the heavier elements forged in the *supernova* should condense. Equally inevitably the first to do so, in a zone still warmed by the sun where lighter, less intractable elements could remain gaseous, were just those weighty solids of which earth and the three other inner planets are mainly composed. Iron and silicon for

the most part, then nickel, chromium, manganese, cobalt and
the rest in just the proportions with which we meet them here
in our globe. So now the whole of the disk out to a radius of
some 150 million miles from the sun was full of whirling fragments of rock and metal, some quite large, many mere particles. Then as the last remnants of gas were thrust out beyond
them, these fragments in their turn began to unite, as though
they hated to be small, isolated and insignificant in the unending
fields of space. In part this was caused by attraction, by the
irresistible gravitational lure of a larger mass for a smaller one,
but it seems that some chemical adhesive was also at work,
perhaps pitch or some other derivative of hydrocarbon, seeing
to it that once one fragment had embraced another, like Brer
Rabbit and the Tarbaby, they should never part.

With minds now able to look back through time to these
events, so great to us, so tiny a part of cosmic history, we can
imagine the flying, spinning mineral masses colliding, attracting, but always coalescing, probably faster and faster as the
gravitational pull of the largest masses became more powerful.
So at last in place of the incoherent fragments, four planetary
bodies came into being, shaped into perfect spheres by the
rapidity of their spinning. Mercury, Venus, Earth and Mars set
off on their paths, on those annual orbits that shape our seasons.
But on the outermost fringe of the zone of heavy condensation,
that is to say in the region outside the orbit of Mars, either
there was no sticking agent or the amount of rock and metal
present was insufficient to draw itself together, so that the fragments continued free and disparate, circling round the sun. They
have continued to circle ever since, the 30,000 asteroids orbiting
between Mars and Jupiter, perpetuating in miniature the vaster
chaos out of which our planets were created.

Two of the inner planets mysteriously acquired satellites.
Mysteriously only because we have not recalled just how it was
done—a curious ignorance when it is considered how much we
believe we know of events immensely more subtle, intricate

13

and remote. The two satellites of Mars are insignificantly small, but the moon, though at first still closer to our earth, was to remain near enough to seem to many men, when at last they had achieved consciousness, to be a worthy female counterpart to the great sun himself. To be, indeed, his spouse, the Queen of Night. The waxing and waning moon has often been a symbol for inconstancy, and her own fate is always in motion. One day she will spiral away from earth and allow herself to be caught instead by the stronger lure of the sun.

While the four small and heavy planets were being built, the outer part of the disk was wheeling ever further from the sun, and in the realms of more than arctic cold beyond the asteroids lighter elements began to condense among the gas. Among all the atoms forged in the *supernova*, those able to condense as water and ammonia were among the most abundant. So it was that when the disk of gas reached distances of between four hundred and one thousand million miles from the sun where the cold forced their condensation, the largest planets in all the solar system were built up by the fusion of smaller masses just as before. But while Jupiter and Saturn first came into being as large conglomerations of these liquids with a relatively small core of light rocks, they seem to have added immensely to their girths by attracting to themselves the hydrogen gas of the disk which still lay all round them. Jupiter is over three hundred times more massive than Earth, Saturn nearly a hundred times; more than half the bulk of these two monsters consists of hydrogen swept up from the disk as they spun and tunnelled through it.

With orbits for ever set so far from their parent star, both planets are cold beyond human endurance; Jupiter perhaps $-120°$ C. on its sunny side; Saturn $-140°$. In both the rock core is probably wrapped in vast ice jackets very many thousands of feet thick, and it is suspected that not only may some of Saturn's satellites be no more than large snowballs, but that its rings, held by many to be the most beautiful spectacle in all the heavens, are formed by glittering sheets of ice crystals.

Beyond these two largest planets, which have been known to men at least since the Sumerians began to chart the stars and probably long before, come Uranus, Neptune and Pluto so far from us that they have been detected by the human eye or mind only in recent centuries. Having so short a relationship with man, and being no part of the familiar celestial presences, we need not think of them, except to say that they were the last creation of the solar disk as it reached its greatest extent, and that they seem to have had their hydrogen whisked away from them by a passing star, probably one born in the same cluster with the sun itself. Perhaps because its final creation was due to the compacting of two large masses, Uranus is freakish in having its spinning axis almost at right angles to those of all brother and sister planets, and Pluto is suspected of being an escaped satellite of Neptune.

This then is the history of the events of four thousand million years ago as they have been recalled by certain minds here on earth. In place of what was a single moderately large star rotating at high speed, there is a considerably smaller and more leisurely one with its nine attendant planets and their thirty satellites, and the ring of asteroids. Most of these planets are spinning on in roughly the same plane as the sun, at right angles to their own orbits. Mercury and Jupiter, the smallest and largest of the family, are almost impeccably upright, but Earth is inclined at about 67° and all the rest are variously slanted, so that they can be imagined as circling the sun with that stately swaying of the axis shown by a top which has been spun at a slight angle to the floor. As for Uranus, it is like a top which has fallen on its side but is still spinning—a thing which can indeed be observed on any nursery floor. As well as this variety in the angle of their spin, the rate is remarkably various. Venus is by far the slowest, so much so that did any form of consciousness exist there it would have to endure a day lasting more than two hundred times as long as ours on Earth; Jupiter and

Saturn on the other hand revolve so fast that they are flattened at the poles and their days are over in about ten hours. Long ago Earth was equally speedy, but it has slowed down to the twenty-four hours which to us on board seems so right and fitting.

Meditating through the mind's eye on this planetary scene, recognizing how each member of the family differs in substance, in size and movement, and how each differs, too, in past history and future prospects, I am seized by a sense of the living informality of this universe. For the whole scheme of things repeats this quality of harmonious variety so evident in our solar system. The casual formation of the *supernovae*, their inevitable end which may, however, come sooner or later; the occasional collision of galaxies; the endless variety of galactic forms, their free, irregular distribution as they wheel through the boundless realms of space. To me it seems comparable to a vast human society, harmonious yet prone to tragedy and accident. More firmly ruled by fixed laws than human society, yet in the end, historically speaking, never quite calculable.

Fred Hoyle insists that in the New Cosmology nothing is arbitrary, nothing due to chance. Yet what he means by this is only that every event appears to be explicable, is not without cause. This is far removed from the picture of mechanical perfection, which, acquired in some belated sub-Newtonian backwater, I long held in my mind. I saw a universe of majestic spheres moving inexorably through perfect orbits, a universe as much a machine as that in the fine new planetarium at Madame Tussaud's. The universe of the New Cosmology is far more sympathetic. Man can almost feel at home in it.

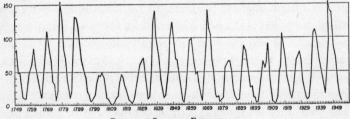

GRAPH OF SUNSPOT FREQUENCY
In units of ten years

BIRTH OF MAN

SO OUR SUN was born, one star among a shower of stars, some four thousand million years ago. For the greater part of this time it has been so nearly constant in size and energy that life on earth could develop continuously in the light and warmth of its rays. Many other of the brightest stars that stud our nights—neighbours that is to say in our own galaxy—are its near contemporaries. For those creatures whose life-span is still hardly more than three score years and ten this seems a vast age indeed. But against the life expectancy of an ordinary star, it is no more than adult. The future life and final fate which men are now foretelling for our sun will be described presently. First let me tell the facts about the being of the sun as they appear to man in A.D. 1962.

Our immediate creator then (for such, I think, this star can properly be called) is removed from us by about ninety-three million miles. It has a diameter of 865,000 miles, and a mass over three hundred thousand times the earth's. Its average density is less than half as much again as that of water, where the earth's (the densest of all the planets) is more than five times as much. It takes about twenty-five of our earthly days to rotate upon its axis, and the direction of its spin is the same as that of all the planets save Uranus, and the same as that followed by the planets as they circle the sun.

So much for measurements and motions, which still, on the scale of the solar system, seem in harmony with the old ideas of the universe as a perfect machine, a vast calendrical timepiece of eternally orbiting spheres. Yet when we look at the stuff and energy of the sun we find instead a physical being with a history and a future, a life-span maintained by the ceaseless transformations of its substance even as the physical being and life-span of a man is maintained by his cells. Indeed, when I was a child it was thought that as the sun was pouring out its treasure of heat, light and other forms of energy with such royal munificence it must gradually exhaust its resources and cool down. I remember feeling very real grief as I pictured earth losing the warmth of its star and becoming more and more arctic until at last all life had withered away and it spun in darkening space, a grey and frozen planet. Now it seems that although the sun is promised a much longer life than was then allowed it, as it grows old it will destroy us not by cooling but by swelling until the earth is cremated. If I no longer feel any real emotion at the prospect, it is not because of the sun's new longevity, not because I have any preference for cremation, but because having lost a child's divine sense of its own eternity, I cannot weep over a holocaust five thousand million years in the future.

The reason for so great a change in our calculations of the prospects before us is our knowledge of nuclear physics. We used to think that the burning of the stars was a chemical process not essentially different from the burning of the gas fires in our grates. Now it is realized that the stupendous pressure and heat of the sun's heart is more than any atom can endure, so that all are breaking down and recombining with a release of energy which is the secret of solar power.

This secret has been discovered here on earth only during the last decade or so. The sun is still composed very largely of the hydrogen of the condensed interstellar gas clouds which gave it birth, together with helium and small amounts of the other elements which, as I have described, were added to its substance

18

by the disintegrated *supernova*. More exactly it contains about one per cent of carbon, nitrogen, oxygen, neon and other non-metallic elements, about a quarter that proportion of metals, ten per cent of helium, while all the rest of its great body consists of hydrogen, that simplest of all elements.

The temperature on the surface of the sun, that is to say at the photosphere where the denser mass of the star terminates and from where most of its light radiates, is between four and five thousand degrees Centigrade. But inwards all the way along the 432,500 miles to the centre of the sphere it grows hotter until it reaches no less than thirteen million degrees. This unimaginable heat is generated to resist the equally tremendous pressure of the overlying layers which is still a million million pounds to the square inch. Heat and pressure maintain the constant sun on which our lives depend. But this fiery furnace at the core of the sun, so much fiercer and more awe-inspiring than any imagined Hell, also holds the secret of the solar energy which men for so long worshipped with an intuitive awareness of their utter dependence upon it. In the heat and pressure of the sun's heart almost all the atoms are shattered, the electrons torn from their nuclei and all alike freed to roam and so to keep this core gaseous in spite of the colossal pressure. In these conditions one process continues steadily. It is the transformation of the elements sought by the alchemists with their pathetic little flames and retorts. A tiny fraction of the star's vast stock of hydrogen is everlastingly being turned into helium. There are three stages in this alchemical process, and as it is as important to terrestrial life as is the conversion of water into steam for an engine, they should perhaps be described. First the single proton of the hydrogen nucleus acquires a second particle—a neutron—producing a form of hydrogen known as a deuteron; during this reaction energy is released in the shape of an electron and a neutrino. In the second stage the deuteron acquires another proton which transforms it into an isotope of helium while emitting radiation, and in the third the uniting of these isotopes creates the normal form of helium nucleus with two protons and two neutrons while releasing two protons. The electron, the radiation and the two protons discharged during these three steps add their energy to the sun and so help to stoke it; the elusive neutrino, on the other hand, ultimately carries its energy away from the sun out into the universe and so is a small item in the debit side of the sun's balance of accounts.

This nuclear furnace, then, has raged at the sun's heart for some four thousand million years, consuming perhaps five hundred million tons of hydrogen in each second of that time. Without it the star would long ago have exhausted itself, so long ago that life on this planet, had it been able to begin, would never have got beyond its first faint tentative stirrings—some amorphous cells moving in the waters, perhaps a skin of algae spreading on their surface. But how in fact has this titanic dance of minutest particles, this atomic Paul Jones, so made itself felt on our tiny sphere ninety-three million miles away that it has been able to raise the minds that have worshipped, analysed and imitated it?

From the central furnace, the energy, of which heat and light are aspects, flows towards the far cooler outer part of the star, travelling at first by radiation (the knocking of particle against particle without change of position) and then also by convection as in the outer part of the sphere the gases boil and seethe. The boiling surface of the sun shows superbly in photographs taken in a single wavelength of light, especially the hydrogen red, when it wreathes and coils and fissures like boiling jam. As the travelling energy reaches the photosphere the mode of travel changes back to radiation, albeit of a different kind from that which it follows on the internal journey. This change is inevitable, for while to maintain its balance the sun has to shed as much energy as the nuclear furnace produces, only by radiation can it travel through the realms of interstellar space where matter, mostly hydrogen, may be as sparse as one single atom to the cubic centimetre. Energy cannot use either of its other two modes of travel, conduction and convection, through space which is so near to a vacuum. But the units, or quanta, of radiation do not require matter for their passage; they pulse through space, each group in its own wavelength, with their eternal regularity and their amazing range from several thousands of metres for radio waves down to less than one thousand millionth of a centimetre for gamma rays.

On leaving the photosphere, however, the sun's radiations do not strike out immediately into space. First they must pass through the star's atmosphere. In the ruddy solar disk of our winter evenings the outline looks sharp as an apple's, yet in fact it is enclosed in a huge envelope of gases. This atmosphere, visible to the unaided earthly eye only at the moment of total eclipse when the moon cuts off the dominating light of the photosphere, is no quiet and mild one like our homely mixture of oxygen and nitrogen, disturbed by nothing worse than a gale or lightning flash. Instead, the inner chromosphere and the outer corona which together envelop the sun consist of fiery gases where atoms of hydrogen and of all, or nearly all, the other elements in the star's substance hurl themselves about and become involved in stupendous flares, titanic falls and magnetic storms so violent that they hurl particles far enough out into space for them to come raining down upon our planet. The flares, explosions of hydrogen, may send their red tongues licking into space over seventy thousand miles; spurting at over a hundred miles a second they could consume the earth utterly, yet, watching them from our safe distance, we see them fade and vanish in a few minutes. Could the men of the past have had the instruments that enable us to watch these superb displays, what legends of divine wrath, what dragon-tales they would have told!

The radiations of light and heat from the photosphere, then, pass through the sun's fiery atmosphere, and are there added to by others coming from the atmosphere itself. For the lower part of the envelope, the chromosphere, emits ultra-violet radiations; the upper part, the corona, emits X-rays. All together the sun's radiations, each keeping to its own beat, undulate out into space. In that space circles our tiny globe, just large enough to catch about one two-thousand-millionths of the radiant solar energy and use it to maintain life and thought. Such is the scientific picture. Yet there is justification, too, for the old view of human kind that the sun shone for the earth's benefit. How clearly it seems to pick us out with its beams, to turn them upon us like some warm and glowing searchlight. How intimate is our relationship with the rising and the setting sun, the one young and rousing, the other serene and preparing us for the night. And in our way we are right, for while there may well be other consciousnesses that see our sun as one star among the innumerable stars of their heaven, a point perhaps in some familiar constellation, it is almost certain that ours is the only full consciousness within the solar system, the only minds supported by the sun's gravitational force, maintained by its energy. Thus we alone know the sun, alone have named it. In this sense it is ours indeed.

The sunlight falls on us in a stream that in our eyes resembles the colour of our ordinary fires. It may look white on the ground, but like all small children who love to show the sun's beaming face in their pictures, we think of it as yellow and symbolize it as golden. Yet for a long time we have known that sunlight can be divided up into 'all the colours of the rainbow', and indeed many more than we can detect in the rainbow. As a child I used to visit a neighbour's house where glass prisms, probably saved from some old chandelier, were left lying on the window bars. On fine days they threw a dozen or more little coloured patches, running from blue through green and yellow to red, on walls and ceiling, on furniture and sometimes on to one's own clothes and skin. As we played, or worked at our sewing class, all these delicious patches wheeled steadily round the room. One which was full on a clock face when it said three o'clock would be sliding off its edge by a quarter past.

Already before this I had been told that a rainbow was caused by the splitting of sunlight by water drops; belonging to a scientific family that information came my way as soon as I was capable of recognizing these lovely arcs. But they were so enchanting, so obviously magical, that I never really accepted this explanation in my heart. But with the coloured patches in my friend's nursery, I did. Nothing I have seen since, not even the elaborate spectrohelioscopes displayed at Conversaziones of the Royal Society, has made me so absolutely aware of the spectrum of sunlight and the wheeling of the sun in the sky.

It still seems to me extraordinary that everyday light is built up from this dazzling range of colours; still more extraordinary that these colours are due to the burning of the chemical elements composing the sun. Each element burns with its own particular wavelengths and therefore with its own particular colours. Salt or any compound of sodium, for example, burns with two wavelengths that make a bright yellow show. So all the colours of the rainbow, and indirectly, all the colours of art and nature, are the product of the sun's chemistry, which, in turn, as we have seen, is the product of cosmic history—the explosion of the *supernova* and the condensing of the star.

Men have in fact learned what the sun is made of by an ingenious way of reading one form of the solar spectrum. Most of the elements present in the mass of the sun are also present at a rather lower temperature in the sun's atmosphere, and as the light from the photosphere passes through the outer envelope they absorb the light on their own exact wavelengths. When the sunbeam is examined through a spectroscope these absorbed wavelengths show as black lines, and it is possible to read off the elements concerned as precisely as if they were written out in chemical formulae.

Most of the radiations streaming out from the photosphere are of wavelengths between eight and four hundred thousandths of a centimetre, which covers the range of visible light. When we say 'visible light' we are speaking wholly subjectively as

23

human beings. We mean the wavelengths to which our human eyes are sensitive, and these eyes, which have evolved in the light of all the innumerable days since sight first dawned in such archaic creatures as the trilobites, are inevitably adjusted to the very light in which they grew. Thus there is no coincidence here, but a pleasing show of the unity of our world and the exactness of our dependence upon the presiding sun.

The wavelengths of visible light preponderate in the sunshine that reaches us as earth-dwellers, but both shorter and longer waves are included in the sun's radiations. X-rays and ultra-violet, coming mainly from the solar atmosphere, are shorter and like all very short waves are deadly to living tissue. They are prevented from reaching the earth's surface in large enough amounts to make life impossible by protective shields which they themselves have created. There are two of these shields—hollow spheres of gas enclosing the planet as the outer spheres enclose the innermost ball in those elegant feats of Chinese ivory carving. The outer one, which encloses us about sixty miles above our heads, is the ionosphere where the atoms of our outer atmosphere have had the electrons struck from the nuclei by the bombardment of X-rays. This layer, made by the X-rays, at the same time serves as a mirror reflecting them back into space and saving life on earth from the lethal radiations which killed so many of the men who first dared to make them artificially. The inner protective sphere is only about fourteen miles overhead and consists of ozone, an altered form of oxygen, which is continually destroyed and re-formed and in the process absorbs the ultra-violet radiation to which it is reacting. Some ultra-violet does in fact penetrate to the earth's surface—indeed, as is well known, as it falls upon our human skins it helps to make vitamin D in our bodies.

Here again there is nothing providential in these shields which today protect us from our sun's short-wave radiations. If they had never been formed, then probably life would still have come into being, but during its evolution would have been adapted to withstand X-rays and ultra-violet, with what strange differences of form we can leave it to someone with the vision of an Hieronymous Bosch to imagine.

The longest of the ultra-violet waves merge into the shortest of those of visible light, the violet, followed by indigo and blue which form the bottom of the sun's colour spectrum as we see it revealed in rainbows, by fountains, diamonds, prisms and all the other agencies which can divide the full chord of our sunlight into its separate notes. When we pass eight hundred thousandths of a centimetre in wavelength, the reds which lie at the opposite extreme from the violets in the spectrum, we pass beyond visible light into the infra-red wavelength which forms a part of the radiations which we recognize as "heat". There is a considerable amount of infra-red radiation from the sun, but a great part of it is absorbed by the water vapour in our atmosphere and so fails to reach the ground. Some, however, does filter through, enough, for example, for it to be possible to sensitize photographic plates to exposures on these wavelengths. Everyone knows that the eye of the infra-red camera is very much more penetrating than our own—that where we see only the haze of distance it can reveal every detail. As infra-red radiations have always reached the earth, it is a little surprising that our eyes did not evolve to make use of them—but presumably our simian ancestors had no need of acute distant vision for the food-gathering at close range which was their livelihood. It is a possibility that birds' eyes are sensitive to infra-red. If so, their extraordinarily keen sight is explained; the hawk diving hundreds of feet to snatch up his prey saw the tiny stirrings of the mouse by means of wavelengths beyond our vision, very much as a dog answers to a supersonic whistle inaudible to the human blower.

While most of the warmth on the earth's surface comes directly from the sun, and an infinitesimally small part from the heat generated by radioactive substances inside the globe, a third source is only indirectly created by solar energy. This is

due to a simple arrangement known as the greenhouse effect—
a unique example of scientific terminology which sets out to
explain instead of obscuring its meaning for the uninitiated.
Everyone has noticed that even when a glasshouse is unheated
it is always, and especially when the sun is shining, agreeably
warmer than the outer air. The glass allows much of the light
and heat of the sunlight to pass through, and they are absorbed
by the plants, soil and all exposed surfaces inside. Plainly they cannot absorb energy indefinitely or they would become red-hot,
but instead of simply reflecting it back within the heat and light
wavelengths, they emit it as infra-red radiation. Now infra-red
cannot pass through glass, and so is held in what in this sense is
well named a conservatory.

The greenhouse is only the earth in microcosm. Everything
on the face of our planet which receives solar energy emits
infra-red radiations just as do the contents of the greenhouse,
and the atmosphere, particularly its water vapour, plays the
part of the glass roof in conserving their warmth. So our great
transparent envelope of gases serves both as a shield and a
blanket for all life on earth. It protects us from the ultra-violet
and X-rays which would destroy our tissues, and conserves the
heat of the infra-red radiations without which we should all
need the coats of polar bears.

The longest wavelengths are those of the radio waves, ranging from about one-tenth of a cm. to several thousand metres.
Only those between one cm. and twenty metres can penetrate
our atmosphere. Although the sun emits radio waves at all times,
they are enormously increased at times of solar disturbance.

Man has not as yet diagnosed these attacks that beset the sun,
but he has discovered that they follow an eleven-year cycle
—taking about 4·6 years to build up to their climax and about
6·7 to return to their minimum. He has also found that a
number of different symptoms are interlinked. They are
magnetic fields, sunspots, prominences, flares and the emission
of high-speed particles and radio waves. Like the earth, the

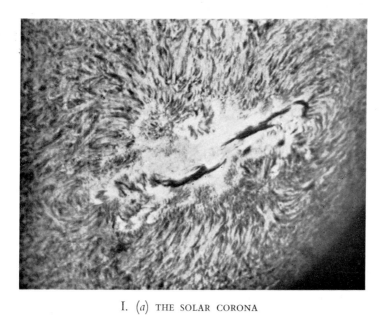

I. (*a*) THE SOLAR CORONA

(*b*) PART OF THE CHROMOSPHERE
showing a disturbed region

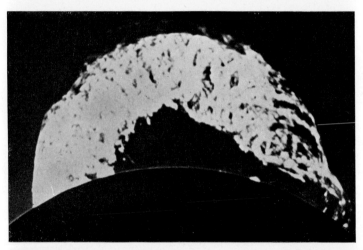

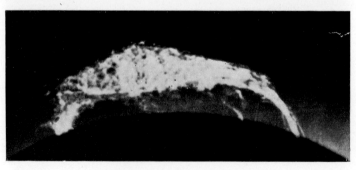

II. SOLAR PROMINENCES

sun has a general magnetic field with lines of force emerging from the north and south poles. Photographs of the corona taken during an eclipse show it short and bristling like a crew-cut over the poles, while round the equator it is soft and cloudy. This general field, however, does not seem to affect the local and short-lived magnetic fields involved in the solar attacks. These probably help to create the tremendous streams of luminous gas in the corona, often curved like the arch of a rainbow, which have been given the unworthy name of prominences. Although they are more luminous than the surrounding parts of the corona, they are in fact less hot, emitting ordinary light waves while the surrounding gases are emitting X-rays and ultra-violet. The cooler gas of the prominences is much of it streaming down over the arch back into the sun, but it plunges in such a way that evidently forces other than the pull of gravitation are controlling it. Almost surely, these forces are magnetic.

The strongest of the local magnetic fields occur in sunspots. These spots, which tend to concentrate on either side of the sun's equator, are probably caused by magnetic forces checking the flow of energy below the photosphere and so lessening the radiation of light. On the other hand the spots are associated with an intense heating of the surrounding parts of the sun's atmosphere, and also with the mighty explosions of violently heated gases in the chromosphere which burst out into the flares that lick out from the corona. These flares are associated in their turn with the hurling out of fast particles into space, most of them reaching the earth in about three days, others moving so fast that they rain upon earth only about half an hour after being spewed from the sun. It is the particles ejected at the time of solar flares that not only cause magnetic storms when they reach our planet but also emit powerful bursts of radio waves. Today all these disturbances trouble man by interrupting his own radio communications, yet in the past they did nothing but delight his eye. For the jets of particles evoke the coloured floodlighting of the heavens known as the aurora. At their finest the Northern and Southern Lights look like swaying translucent curtains of green and red and white, miraculously hung in thin air. Usually they appear only to those who live not very far from the poles, but at times when the sun is most violently disturbed by sunspots and flares they may be visible over the entire globe. The aurora is due to oxygen atoms in the rarefied atmosphere a hundred miles and more above the earth becoming charged with energy by the hurtling particles and releasing it again (without further collisions) in the form of radiation. One of the most brilliant displays of the present century was in 1938, a year when sunspots were many and powerful. Towards the end of January all the peoples of the northern hemisphere had only to look up at night to see the sky shimmering with a silken sheen.

Our planet journeying through space encounters one other form of bombardment which deserves to be mentioned even though its main source is not a solar one. When cosmic rays were named they were believed to be a very short-wave radiation, but now that we have discovered them instead to be particles of extraordinarily high energy, the old name with its stirring science-fiction flavour has not been relinquished. The sun at times of upheaval does itself emit cosmic rays of relatively low energy, and inevitably some of these are intercepted by the earth. But most of them, including all those of the most violent energy, enter the solar system from outer space—a gift from the galaxy at large. The particles are mainly protons, but also comprise the nuclei of heavy elements such as iron. When, like other particles but with far greater force, they strike our protective wrapping of atmosphere, they completely shatter the atomic nuclei, and while they themselves never penetrate to the ground, showers of mesons, the peculiar fragments resulting from these infinitesimal yet mighty collisions, drift down among us much as a few broken snowflakes will drift through the canopy of a tree.

28

How evident it has now become that the sun is no sharply defined sphere, no simple mechanical part! Indeed the conception we shall discover among the Egyptians of the sun's rays ending in hundreds of little hands showering life upon earth, has much truth in it. We must see our star as a body with no hard and fast outline, a body whose enormously dense core merges into outer parts of boiling gases which in turn give way to an atmosphere more rarefied but still full of atoms and atomic fragments moving at vast speeds and charged with stupendous energy. This atmosphere is made tempestuous by the stress of magnetic fields, the rising and falling of hotter and cooler gases, the explosion of tongues of fire tens of thousands of miles into space. Beyond this again the sun sends its endless quanta of radiation rippling throughout the planetary system and yet further, while from time to time jets of particles are blown like sand-blast among them.

At two thousand million miles from the sun its light is still strong enough to allow the reading of fine print—were there readers on Uranus, which orbits at about this distance. More than twice as far away, Pluto is bathed in a faint solar light, while outside our system altogether, beings on other planetary systems may even now be studying our sun as a component in some to them familiar constellation; others further and further away may be seeing it as a smaller and smaller point of light until, for the most distant, it merges into the powdery shine of a Milky Way.

To complete the picture of universal interdependence we have to recall that as well as all these emanations from the sun there is also the inward pull of its gravitational force. This invisible bond which holds all the planets in their courses is of such tremendous power that even for the earth alone it is equal to the strength of a bar of tempered steel five thousand miles in diameter.

Earth, then, as a minute spherical grain in this beautifully interacting play of force and energy and matter in space, catches its own infinitesimal share of the solar radiation, and during the course of twenty-four hours almost every part of the globe's surface, and all things living on that surface, are in turn exposed to the radiation as they are lifted up from the cone of night, turned full into the sunshine and then lowered once more into darkness. This gift of energy received during the daylight hours has been used to create, develop, maintain, life and consciousness. Today, as for hundreds of millions of years, the task of trapping the sun's energy and diverting it into the veins of life has been performed by leaves. Leaves sword-shaped and heart-shaped, simple and intricate, smooth and corrugated, waxy and hairy, perpetual and deciduous—but nearly all green. Unlike the animal kingdom, plants can feed on pure carbon and this they catch from the atmosphere, from the carbon dioxide always present in small quantities in the invisible gases in which we are immersed. The leaf wantoning in the air is eating away as steadily as a sheep in a field. The pigment which gives it its green colour is contained in neat little star-like containers in the leaf's central layers. This chlorophyll absorbs the radiant energy (which only eight minutes before was leaving the face of the sun) and with it breaks down the carbon dioxide gas, and the water sucked from the ground, combines them as sugar (carbon with hydrogen and oxygen) and releases the surplus oxygen into the air.

How wonderful it is that between the harsh mineral mass of the earth and the furious nuclear furnace of the sun this tender foliage should be able to mediate, to bend radiation to the milder processes of chemical reaction, chemical reaction to the familiar creativeness of plant and animal life. In the barren infancy of the earth there seems to have been little free oxygen in the atmosphere; it was supplied, as it is still maintained, in the countless hosts of chlorophyll sacs held to the sun by the vegetation that greens the face of our planet. Without this vast and beautiful gasworks the existence of man and his fellow animals would be impossible. And it is not only for the oxygen to vitalize our blood that we depend upon the plants; far more obviously the greater part of terrestrial animal life depends directly or indirectly upon them for bodily nourishment. Only some of the water dwellers could survive without them as they did when the earth was younger. Plants provide the rest of us flesh-and-blood creatures with the food we eat as well as the air we breathe. Their roots raise the chemical elements and compounds from the soil, turning them, together with the carbon leaf-snatched from the air, into the substances that animal bellies can digest. And so those elements which were created by the exploding of a giant star are compounded into our bodies for a while before they are returned to the earth.

This, then, is the manner in which the sun supports life day by day. As the burning of coal, gas, electricity provides the energy needed to set in train the chemical processes of cooking which make food palatable to man, the nuclear burning of our star provides the energy to make carbon palatable to the plants, and so sets in train the whole process of building that leads from elemental atoms through more and more highly organized molecules to living cells and on to the butterfly, the elephant, and to the scientist who mentally breaks down these same processes and the poet who synthesizes them. This goes on perpetually in the eternal present, but it has to be seen also in the perspective of cosmic time. That is to say a comparable (though quite distinct) building chain initiated by the sun's energy has occupied a considerable part of the four thousand million years of planetary history, creating butterfly and elephant, scientist and poet, from the atoms and molecules of a naked mineral earth and its enshrouding gases.

When, where and how did life originate on this planet? These scientific questions are trivial beside the great philosophical question of 'Why?', but they are more within reach of answers. In fact the answer to the first can never be exact, probably never more exact than it is at present, for the reason that life itself cannot be defined. Just as the colours of the sun's spectrum merge gradually into one another, so do chemical processes into the processes of life. So that when human minds, those most rare fruits of life, attempt to divide them, they will never agree where the division should be made. We as yet know little of the intermediate forms which preceded the earliest certainly-recognizable forms of life, but we know some of their modern counterparts. Indeed they are only too familiar. We have all of us given them lodging, have known how they can cloud our thoughts and rack our bodies. The viruses, too minute to be caught in the finest filters, are alive in the sense that they perpetuate themselves by breeding; on the other hand they lapse into purely crystalline forms and can only become breeding organisms in a particular chemical environment.

The man who was one of the founders of biochemistry, the study of the chemistry of life, and whose place in the grand sequence of life on earth is of great significance to me as he initiated my own, believed the very lowest qualification for life is that it should be able to show 'a dynamic equilibrium in a polyphasic system'. This definition of my father's—which implies that living matter must have a distinction of parts—is probably as good as any other. It would certainly include the virus in its active phases.

When in our quest for origins we believed it certain that the earth began as a glowing, molten mass, it was assumed that an immensely long period of cooling had to be allowed for before the first stirrings of life could have been even possible. Now, however, that we think the globe was compounded from lumps of cold matter and developed its internal heat largely from radioactive substances, no such waiting period is necessary. Indeed at least one most distinguished thinker believes that the first steps towards the generation of life may have been taken on the particles of matter circling in space before they came together to form our planet. One reason for this idea is that the ultra-violet radiation, which all agree is most likely to have provided the generating energy, would have been far more abundant in the solar belt before the earth was built. But if as is probable there was little free oxygen in the atmosphere of the infant earth, there would have been no ozone canopy to screen it from the ultra-violet light and enough of this radiation would have fallen on the earth's surface to do the work of generation.

If, then, it is agreed that it is more probable as well as aesthetically more satisfying to think that earthly life began on this globe and not in space, its beginnings must have been between five hundred million and four thousand million years ago. Before trying to narrow these enormous limits we have to imagine the nature of those beginnings, a task immensely difficult for those whose minds are not accustomed to moving in the intricate, microscopic world of biochemistry. One thing seems certain: the central figure of this book was the begetter. In that sense the sun, *Sol Invictus*, is Our Father in Heaven.

We have to imagine, then, the bare planet, built from its ninety or so elements, bathed in sunlight, including an abundance of that wavelength known as ultra-violet. Striking upon relatively simple compounds built from a few common substances such as water, ammonia or marsh gas, the ultra-violet light imbued them with the energy to form far more complex molecules. It also gave them a store of internal energy which in the cool conditions of the earth's face was not dissipated but led to the creation of ever more elaborate molecular structures until at last there emerged conglomerations which we can recognize as living organisms.

All forms of existing life depend very largely upon proteins. For this reason, and because they are composed almost entirely of the very common elements carbon, hydrogen, oxygen and nitrogen arranged in a great variety of designs, it has often been assumed that protein molecules were of prime importance for the origins of life. Architects and craftsmen raised the lovely and significant Gothic cathedrals from stone quarries, from mere lumps hacked from the mineral skin of the planet; the mysterious designing power behind life created its far more wonderful and various forms from materials equally simple.

Yet although it is tempting to assume that proteins have always been an indispensable part of life it would be presumptuous to do so until exploring consciousness has penetrated into its remotest past far more deeply than at present. It may be that many other biochemical foundations were tried out and eliminated before protein metabolism proved to be the most successful. It may be, in fact, that the Darwinian struggle for the survival of the fittest among animals and plants was preceded by a comparable one among the most elementary biochemical processes. For even these faint, barely organic forms of existence, compared with which an amoeba would be a genius, may well have competed for materials, for energy, and above all for the ideal mechanical and chemical environment. Odd survivals in the metabolisms of certain ancient species support this guess that the chemical basis of life may at first have been more varied. If so, then perhaps this competition in biochemical efficiency went on until life had reached a degree of organization comparable to that of the present self-nourishing bacteria, by which time the protein metabolisms were universally established and the evolution of plants and animals could start on its long and adventurous course.

We can now make our minds grapple with chronology on an astronomical scale and determine between what limits life is most likely to have begun. For the unambitious water creatures of the Cambrian Age to evolve into such recent types as elephants, horses and men has taken five hundred million years. So much the fossils of the rocks have recorded for us. Probably at least as long was needed for life to advance from a possible bacterial stage to that of the worms and jellyfish of the pre-Cambrian rocks—the earliest imprints of life to have been detected by the human eye. Thus if earth's life began on her

34

own surface it can be said with some certainty that it was between one and four thousand million years ago. Is it possible to be more precise (indeed, a range of three thousand million years can hardly be said to be precise at all)? As unusual associations of environment, mechanical support and assembled molecular materials were needed—though always the sun was flinging down the necessary energy—it may well have taken an enormously long time for the true life processes to start. On the other hand, once having established themselves, they may have colonized a virgin planet quite rapidly; rapidly, that is to say, if one is thinking on a scale on which a million years are like an evening gone.

Perhaps, then, the step from elaborate chemical to relatively simple biochemical processes took place a few hundred million years on either side of two thousand million years ago. Before that, for something like half its existence, the earth remains a subject for the geologist, the chemist and physicist alone. Year after empty year it made its journey round the sun; day after day it completed its gyration. This was the time when the days were shorter, perhaps at first lasting no more than ten hours, until gradually the speed of the earth's spin was slowed by the drag of the moon using the earth's tides as a brake. This was the time, too, when the nights would have been more brilliant because our satellite was nearer to earth. Moonrise then would have been most majestical; a truly vast silver disk must have lifted itself above the naked horizon, casting harsh rock shadows on to vacant ground.

Yet constancy and change alike were meaningless. Not only was there no consciousness to respond, not even the faint consciousness of a leaf turning to the sun, there was nothing but the streaming away of energy into space. Always one cheek of the globe was steeped in sunlight, but even if some trace of its energy were caught for a moment in the building of a chemical structure, it soon broke down again and dispersed. For it is only life which casts its magical nets to catch energy and use it

35

for the creation of new forms. Without it earth travelled and spun and the sun's rays were cast back into space.

It is not my intention here to tell the evolutionary history of life on earth. I have already attempted it, and attempted it moreover from the same point of view which is of significance here—that is to say from the point of view of the evolution of consciousness. I will only say that I have not repented my heretical views that natural selection has not been the primary and fundamental shaper of living forms. Life, it is now estimated, is quite likely to exist on one hundred thousand million planetary systems in our galaxy alone. To me it seems evident that all we life-clad spheres are part of some far larger system developing with all the inevitability of a peacock growing from an egg. If this is some form of vitalism, then I am a vitalist. And I see the function of our part of the system as being the development of consciousness. If that is teleological, then I am certainly a teleologist. Both vitalist and teleologist are dirty names in natural science, where the idea of intention in nature is abhorrent. Yet it is in fact very difficult to distinguish between intention and more or less predetermined process. There can be a theoretically infinite regress of patterned evolutionary sequences. The development of the individual creature from the single-celled ovum; the evolution of the species during the span of life on earth, and the evolution of some cosmic 'creature' in which our galaxy with its countless planetary points of consciousness is playing its small part. Larger and larger in scale, each may be patterned by a previous evolution. Just as it is hard to deny that the 'purpose' of the fertilized ovum is to become a peacock or an ant or whatever it may be, so in my view it is impossible to be sure that it was not the 'purpose' of the original molecules and solar radiation to lead to life and consciousness on earth. And so on at every scale. Yet ultimately, of course, one comes up against the first or last cause and the clash with natural science.

No, I do not intend to repeat the story of the evolution of

earthly life in all its marvellous variety of species, but only to call attention to one aspect of it: the continuing relationship between the sun and these its progeny. The supply of energy for chemical reactions so essential in the first begetting, only became more varied as organisms attained higher forms. The most important became the process already described, the stimulation of chlorophyll to enable plants to pasture on the air. Then there is the direct dependence of our reptilian fore-bears (and their surviving representatives) on the warmth of sunshine. During the night hours, when earth had carried them out of its reach, they became torpid; as useless without their source of energy as a car without petrol, an electric element without current. As well as such greater debts of earth to the sun there are hosts of smaller yet equally vital ones; man and many other animals, for example, would perish if there were no sunshine to cause our bodies to manufacture vitamin D. I still remember, though I was myself a small child at the time, my father's mingled happiness and anger when he came back from a visit to Vienna after the First World War. He had seen the city sick and suffering as a result of the Allied blockade, and he had seen the hospital where his pupil and colleague Harriet Chick was exposing half-starved children naked to the sun and the cruel symptoms of rickets were being checked by the radiation.

Then again the sun has always had a momentous mechanical role to play in drawing water up into the atmosphere, where it condenses again and rains back on to the land surface of the globe that without it would be utterly desert. Thus nearly all the vegetation, on which so much other life depends, is itself doubly dependent on the sun: for carbon and water—its food and drink.

Only a mixture of good sense and ignorance saves me from telling of very many other ways in which the evolution and maintenance of earthly life are at the mercy of our presiding star. Instead I want to consider one highly distinctive form of our total dependence which has special significance for the growth of consciousness. Human beings who have been born blind can develop their full mental powers as members of society, but this is made possible by their fellows who play the part of their eyes, helping them through speech and touch to project an image of the world in the perpetual darkness where they are condemned to dwell. It is unthinkable that the human mind or any but the most elementary forms of consciousness could have dawned without seeing and the light which is a part of it.

Some very simple animals, even those with only one cell to their name, have taken the first step towards sight in being sensitive to light and moving either towards or away from it. Creatures of this type would have been the first to make their faint response as the globe spun them from daylight into darkness. Their sensitivity is general to the whole of their minute being, with no hint of an eye. The next step was taken by organisms still small and unambitious in function which possessed, however, limited patches on their bodies that were chemically sensitive to light. These patches, moreover, were supplied with nerve cells to convey the message of the chemical change by an infinitesimal electric charge to muscle cells able to cause movement. Creatures which made this important pioneer advance towards sight included worms and other backboneless inhabitants of the ancient oceans—in fact the very creatures which left the earliest traces of themselves in the pre-Cambrian rocks, as though to symbolize the fact that as they could receive faint impressions so too could they make them.

These worms and others equipped like them could not only respond to light, but could also sense from what direction it was coming, and could even be aware of movement if it caused a shadow to fall across the sensitive patch. Indeed if the patch were large enough they may even have registered some vague intimation of form. So now, thousands of millions of years after its birth, the solar system was beginning to see itself. In the utterly unreflective awareness of sunrise and sunset, of a passing cloud, of the movement of a brother worm or of drifting algae, these faint marine presences had started on the way which was to lead on the one hand to all the glories of our arts and on the other to the great eyes of Palomar and Mount Vernon where men look out not only at the solar system, not only at their own galaxy, but into distances where time and space and receding galaxies stretch beyond sight and beyond comprehension.

The earliest creatures to leave clear fossil impressions of true eyes were the trilobites, crustaceans ranging in size from a pinhead to as much as eighteen inches long, which were abundant in the Cambrian seas and represented the highest achievement of life in their Age. They had two compound eyes, each with many tiny lenses, and a median eye as well, and so mechanically were well equipped for vision and had adequate nervous arrangements to allow them to transmit what they saw into action. With their lenses they could probably not only see in some detail the dead and living organisms on which they fed, but through focusing would be able roughly to judge distance. Yet while some trilobites allowed the sunlight streaming through the clear water to illuminate their hunting and scavenging, other species forwent it, spending dark lives eyeless in the mud.

The trilobites, lords of creation though they were in Cambrian times, were invertebrates and had nothing that could be called a true brain. What they saw sent electric messages for action—for the scuttle of limbs or the snapping of jaws, practically nothing more. With the backboned animals and their perfectly unified central nervous system the control point grew into a true brain and the intimate link between sight and mind had been forged. It is indeed significant, even if only symbolically, that in the embryonic growth of the vertebrates the receptive part of the eye, the retina and its surroundings, bud outward from the brain instead of sinking inward from the skin as do those of the invertebrates.

From this stage onwards not only was the animal able to see all that surrounded him on the surface of the earth, the clouds, moon and stars, and the great illuminator himself, but to form clear inner pictures of things seen and store them as canvases are stored in the vaults of some vast gallery. So great is this power in man that he can draw, paint, carve, the remembered scene or thing when it is not before his eyes. What is more (and man himself does not know how), when eyes are closed and he lies in darkness intensely vivid scenes project themselves before his sleeping mind, lit, it seems, by the glow of remembered sunlight.

Since the days of the trilobites very many kinds of eyes have been evolved, suiting the habits of their possessors and enabling them to see the world in their own particular modes. There are differences in the breadth and depth of vision, and between those animals which, like ourselves and all the primates, have forward-looking eyes that give a single stereoscopic picture, and those with eyes looking sideward, each with its own picture.

More significant in the relationship between eye and sun is the division between creatures of the day and of the night. Just as the black feet of the swan make him a clumsy fool until he returns to his element, so the eyes of many birds, beasts and insects keep them all but helpless until the sun has set. These contrasting capacities depend upon a subtle and imperfectly understood combination of the structure and chemistry of the retina—that part of the eye corresponding to the sensitized plate or film of the camera. A retina can be composed of one or other of two types of cells or from a mixture of the two. The kind known as rods make a simple response to light and enable the eyes equipped with them to see by moon and starlight and even by the faint glimmer of our darkest earthly nights. The cones, in contrast, are adapted for acute vision in bright light and for discrimination between colours. Thus among the birds, all those that stir only with the dawn are supplied largely or wholly with cones, while the owl (that messenger of the children of darkness) has large numbers of rods. Like most mammals, man has both rods and cones, but one limited patch on the human retina, the macula, is tight-packed with cones, and it is probably this device that enables us to enjoy so fine a range of colours.

But sight does not depend only on this mechanical action of cells and of the nerve fibres that carry their signals. On exposure to light, a chemical change takes place in the eye just as it does in the silver bromide on the camera plate. But whereas the bromide is affected once and for all, in our eyes the chemical substances instantly recompose themselves for a fresh exposure. When the light has been relatively strong this process is not always complete; we are all familiar with the ghostly image of the bedside lamp after we have switched it out at night, of the window with its panes after we have looked away from it.

The chemical which reacts in the rod cells has been isolated and given the name of visual purple, a stuff closely related to vitamin A. Visual purple bleaches out in full daylight, but as soon as the eye is shaded it quickly renews it, and it is this renewal which we await as we stand bewildered on first stepping into the darkness. After half an hour the rods in our retinae have again been steeped in visual purple and have become ten thousand times more sensitive to light. Indeed the human eye when fully adapted to the dark can appreciate a smaller amount of light than any existing photo-electric cell.

In spite of all scrutinizing of eyes by eyes, the chemical substance in the cones, which must surely exist to correspond with the visual purple of the rods, has not as yet been surely detected. The chemistry of our daylight vision remains at present unknown.

With colours and the enormous pleasure, as well as utility, they have for us, we are in the presence of another of the great gifts of the sun. While many creatures see the world in monochrome like an ordinary photograph, others respond to a few (a bee can recognize blue but not red), apes and monkeys to a much larger number, and the normal man can distinguish as many as one hundred and sixty shades when he looks at them in sunlight. It is now a familiar thought that colour is not a property of the thing seen, but is created partly by the light waves, partly by the eye of the beholder. Colour leaves the brightest flowers after sunset; a proportion of every generation of men is born unable to differentiate between red and green.

The colours we enjoy are given to us by the spectrum of visible light, by the 'colours of the rainbow', and therefore are due to wavelength. One of those huge scarlet poppies blazing in the sun is in fact absorbing all the blue and green wavelengths and a part of the yellow, while reflecting a small proportion of the yellow and all the red into our eyes. The fine black patches at the base of each petal are absorbing the whole colour spectrum and giving us back nothing, while the petals of marguerites growing beside the poppies are absorbing nothing but reflecting the whole of the sun's rays with the white effect that the totality of the colours of the visible spectrum produces in our eyes.

This much, then, is clear, if not simple. Colours as we see them come from the different wavelengths of the solar radiation, which in turn come from the different elements burning in the sun's furnace. But how our eyes convey them to the brain, so that they can be used for road signals, exploited for advertisements, brilliantly employed for imaginative effect in paintings, remains almost completely unknown to the brains that respond to them with such exactitude. Almost certainly it is a combination of structure (the rods and cones of the retina) and wavelength—sensitive chemicals comparable to visual purple but not yet discovered in spite of most patient search. Yet even if in time the seeing devices of eye and brain are fully understood, the greater mystery surely remains. The reader has only to look at whatever scene is before him and try to fathom just what he is doing, just what is happening as he receives this image of an outer world which is immediately a part of his whole consciousness (with associative thoughts streaming off in all directions), to be made aware of this central mystery.

Birds may have a much keener vision than men, perhaps being able to see by wavelengths down to infra-red, but although they are probably well aware of colours, as is suggested both by the gorgeous plumage of many male birds and by the fondness for coloured scraps shown by such birds as magpies and weaver birds, it is unlikely that they are able to register anything approaching the human range. Our superiority is due in small part to our eyes which have retinae well packed with cones as well as rods, but in far larger part, surely, to our uniquely elaborated brains. This leads back to one of the most fascinating questions of human evolution. These unique brains grew in the men-apes and ape-men of the Pliocene and Pleistocene Ages, when, if the crude law of natural selection is to be accepted, they were brought into being solely for survival in an animal, and subsequently near-animal, hunting life in the savannahs and forests, the wild hills and tundras of the natural world. What an amazing chance, then, that this gathering of birds' eggs, frogs and reptiles, this pursuit of young animals, this digging up of roots, this hunting and gnawing of flesh, should produce the ear of Mozart and Beethoven, the mental fibre of Socrates and Einstein, the eye of the great colourists— of Renoir, say, and Van Gogh. Here I am once more teetering on the teleological brink.

There is not very much more to tell about the physical relationship of earth and sun. It is almost time to turn to the mental relationship that grew with man. Looking out of the June window before beginning this fresh chapter, I see the soft red roofs of the village, the cedars standing like wide pagodas against the sky, and I hear the chirping, calling and singing of birds enjoying the evening light, an occasional bark or shout. How secure it is, how substantial and long-established, this Warwickshire at the centre of England. But now, as though meeting an old friend on an X-ray screen, I am confronted with an altogether different presence. All the trunks and leaves, the bricks and tiles, no longer named and outlined and substantial but vast aggregates of atoms, the atoms themselves dissolving into pure energy. The clear evening air, too, shows as only less crowded with particles, and through them pulse endless inter-flowing tides of waves. Waves of heat and light pouring from the sun, radio waves streaming from all over England, sound waves coming from vibrating chords within those brief organizations of living energy, the birds, the dogs, the children. Yes, the air is full of radiations and vibrations either shattering against or flowing unimpeded through the once seemingly solid atomic masses of the earth—those walls, those roofs and trees. They are changing the chemicals in my eyes, trembling the stretched membranes in my ears, sending electric currents flickering through my brain and so stimulating in the midst of all this matter, this energy, the mysterious powers of consciousness.

It has endured for four thousand million years, this relationship between sun and earth, and for at least a quarter of that time their living offspring have been raised between them. What will the end of the story be? Our star being of moderate size it happily has a long calm middle age before it, long enough surely to outlast the needs of our species. Yet even if men are not involved directly in the end of the relationship it has an interest for us. It seems that after the sun has lived a little more than as long again as its present age it will reach a turning-point in its career after which it will become far more turbulent. So much hydrogen will by then have turned into helium in the heart of the sun that the pressure balance will become disturbed in a number of ways. At first it will cause the sun to swell, which will oblige its surface to cool somewhat even while it emits more light. The helium core, which will by then have been for some time stagnant and of even temperature, will itself begin a nuclear conflagration which must lead to an internal explosion. Thereafter the decline will be more like that of an old man. The star will shrink, turn white and far less bright, at last perhaps to cool gradually down until it becomes a lump of matter with no energy to give to life or any other such adventure. But the end of the earth will come long before this final solar senility. When the sun begins to swell and grow brighter, that is to say in about another five thousand million years, it will quite soon give this planet a climate with an average temperature of about one hundred degrees Centigrade. Life by then will have boiled away. As the radiation increases earth itself will be vaporized, and before it begins to contract again the sun will have swollen to two or three hundred times its present girth, which means that it will reach the size of the orbits of Mercury and Venus and perhaps even that of Earth itself.

This seems a violent and cruel end to what, as we shall see, has been very much like a love affair between star and satellite. It is as hard to accept as our own personal deaths. And let it be admitted that it is far less certain. For perhaps the minds of men in A.D. 1962 are still in error. Or perhaps events on some other scale of existence may intervene.

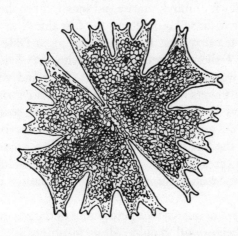

CHLOROPHYLL
Granules shown by the microscope

SUN FATHER AND EARTH MOTHER

Now at last mind was dawning, raised between sun and earth. Where for so long light had beaten back into space, reflected from the lifeless surface of land and water, where, later, eyes had evolved to use light and focus images of their surroundings for animals in marvellous variety, now between image and physical reaction came the pause of thought. Faint, fleeting, indecisive at first, but growing always stronger and more absolute as man found himself and lost nature. The pause that enabled him to shape and to name.

In that dawn of mind, sunrise and sunset, if not the sun itself, seem likely to have been among the first things to have been named by the first men. Even such a being as Oldoway Man, one of the earliest known hominids, who over half a million years ago was catching lizards, snakes, frogs and young birds with quick fingers and crunching them in his enormous jaws, must always have been very much aware of the passage of the sun across the gorge where he lived. He may conceivably even have used the lips stretched over his ape-like snout to frame sounds to express its coming and going. If so, then here already was a step in creation through *logos*—the separation of day and night.

I have tried to imagine the perceptions of the sun experienced by these beings still shoulder-deep in animality. I am not ashamed to admit that it is easier for women to empty their minds of all thought, yet even so this conscious effort to return to a state so near the unselfconscious must defeat itself. One can only recapture something of the simple and unchanging sensuousness of it, of heat on the bare body, of dazzling skies screened as though by a peaked cap by the overhanging brows, of shade eagerly sought, of the pursued animal lurking in the shadows. One can imagine perceptions differentiated enough to provoke some dim awe at the approach of sunset over wide African landscapes, and even for the sun itself as something for ever out of reach and with the power to blind those who would stare at it when it burned overhead.

I believe, too, that while Oldoway Man and his like were very much aware of the sun in the outer world as an arbiter of day and night and of the movements of their prey and of themselves they also knew an inner world, below the threshold of consciousness, where, indelibly imprinted, was the inheritance of the aeons of nights and days to which life had been exposed since its beginnings. So profound was this inner vision of light and darkness, that it emerged with thought and language as one of the most powerful and universal of all the symbols of mankind. From our first recorded utterances onward, we find light symbolizing the good, the rational, ourselves, and darkness the irrational, the evil, our enemies. The children of light and the children of darkness. This imagery dwells in every one of us, constantly coming to our lips, and flooding out in poetry and music. Nowadays perhaps we envisage it more often as the light of the conscious, and the darkness of the unconscious, mind. But always this hidden memory of the unnumbered days and nights to which life has been exposed on this turning globe is strong within us.

I have said that a kind of awe may have been felt even by the earliest men for this unreachable, eye-dazzling presence in their skies, for its journey from horizon to horizon and for the golden transformation it could work upon the world at the time of its nightly disappearance. Yet it is unlikely that they or their descendants for many thousands of generations could have formulated either religious or heroic ideas concerning it. Their power over mental images, thoughts and words was too tenuous.

Yet one of the great events in human history, which took place in this still remote time, may have had an influence on the dawning mental relationship between man and sun. Before the onset of the second glaciation, primitive humans such as those who lived in the caves of Choukoutien near Peking, had over-come the animal's instinctive terror and won mastery over fire. They may not have known how to kindle fire, but they main-tained and controlled it. At once, surely, even the dimmest minds must have recognized an affinity between the flames on their hearths and the sun above them? Not only was there the identity of colour, but also the same sense of heat striking the naked body, the same defeat of darkness. When, much later, man obtained pure gold from rocks and rivers, as soon as he saw it gleaming in his hand he was to identify it with the sun. The same thing in a simpler, less symbolic way, must have happened as the hunter looked into the heart of his fire or saw it from afar. Yet, practically, the dependence of the fire-owners on the sun was lessened. Now, if they would, they could stay awake and active when all sunlight had faded; they could pene-trate caves where sunlight had never been.

I believe that a third glaciation must have spread and gone again before men began to enact the rites and weave the tales which were to turn our star-creator into a hero and a divinity. It may be that Neanderthal Man made the first faint ritual gesture. That he had imagination is shown by the burial of the dead with food and weapons as provision for a life after death, and by the eating of human brains as though with the thought of participating in greatness. In the most ceremonious of Neanderthal burials, that of La Chapelle-aux-Saints in the Dordogne, the body had been orientated east and west.

Whether this was chance, or whether it represents the beginning of that potent and still living idea of identifying life and death, sunrise and sunset, burial and the sun's descent into the underworld, who shall say? If East and West had this significance for him, then Neanderthal Man initiated a symbolic ritual which was to continue through all history.

Yet even if he did in truth initiate this ritual observance, even though he did possess some imaginative power, I cannot think that he was articulate enough to create myths and tales. Here the blossoming would have come with the Upper Palaeolithic peoples who succeeded his race, their heads filled with the fully evolved brain of *Homo sapiens* but also with mental innocence. As hunters they need not be supposed to have worshipped the sun. That was to come later with the cultivation of the soil and its plants. There is no trace among all the works of art made by these gifted hunters of the last glacial age of any solar symbol, or indeed of anything which could be intended to represent sun, moon or stars or the heavens at large. Instead they carved the figures of women whose great thighs, breasts and bellies show that already they expressed not only wonder at woman's power to create new life, but fecundity itself and the birth in man's mind of the image of the Great Mother. Her splendid figure was, indeed, the first religious image of a symbolic kind to be shaped by our species.

The absence of any solar portrait or symbol in Palaeolithic art may not mean that the sun had absolutely no part in it. A rite practised among the pygmies of the Congo warns against any such assumption. Frobenius was travelling through the jungle with several of these skilful and brave little hunters when, towards evening, a need arose for fresh meat. The white man asked his companions if they could kill an antelope. They were astonished at the folly of the request, explaining that they could not hunt successfully that day because no proper preparation had been made; they promised to go hunting the next morning instead. Frobenius, curious to know what their preparations might be, got up before dawn and hid himself on the chosen hill-top. All the pygmies of the party appeared, three men and a woman, and presently they smoothed a patch of sand and drew an outline upon it. They waited; then, as the sun rose, one of the men fired an arrow into the drawing, while the woman raised her arms towards the sun and cried aloud. The men dashed off into the forest. When Frobenius approached the place, he found that the drawing was that of an antelope and that the arrow stood in its neck. Later, when the hunting party had returned with a fine antelope shot through the neck, some of them took tufts of its hair and a calabash of blood, plastered them on the drawing and then wiped it out. Joseph Campbell adds, 'The crucial point of the pygmy ceremony was that it should take place at dawn, the arrow flying into the antelope precisely when it was struck by a ray of the sun. For the sun in all hunting mythologies is a great hunter. He is the lion whose roar scatters the herds, whose pounce at the neck of the antelope slays it . . . he is the orb whose rays at dawn scatter the herds of the night sky, the stars.' The return of the hair and blood is, of course, propitiation, to secure that the death shall be made good. Even though the surviving Palaeolithic paintings are in caves where the womb of darkness rather than the ray of the sun must have been sought, it is not impossible that their makers carried out comparable magical rites in the open.

Whether or no the sun played any part in their hunting magic, it seems likely to have entered their lore just as it did their everyday lives. Indeed, those peoples who lived in a Europe still glaciated and exposed to a bitter climate must have begun to know that delight in the sun, perhaps even that craving for it, which seizes us northerners today. Surely when the hanging glaciers began to groan, crack and tumble with the spring, when the river ice broke and grass grew for the game herd, then the sunny day must have brought a fine lifting of the spirits, perhaps have given the signal for dancing and song.

Just as they were the first painters and sculptors, probably these Stone Age hunters were the first true story-tellers, composing such tales as modern hunters love to hear. And in this lore the sun probably played its part not as any kind of divinity, but on an equal footing with animals, spirit-ancestors and human heroes. This is how our star is regarded by the native Australians. Among them there is a Sun Totem no lower but no more exalted than those of the Kangaroos, Witchetty Grubs or Honey Ants. In their legends it plays such a part as is found in the Aranda bandicoot myth. All Australian myths are lovingly wedded to a particular territory, and this one is concerned with Ilbalintja, which is also a Sun Totem-centre.

In the very beginning everything was resting in perpetual darkness: night oppressed all the earth like an impenetrable thicket. The Gurra ancestor—his name was Karora—was lying asleep in everlasting night at the very bottom of the soak of Ilbalintja; as yet there was no water in it and all was dry ground. Above him the soil was red with flowers and overgrown with many grasses; a great *tnatantja* [ceremonial pole] was swaying over him. This *tnatantja* had sprung from the midst of the bed of purple flowers which grew over the soak of Ilbalintja. At its root rested the head of Karora himself; from thence it mounted up towards the sky as though it would strike the very vault of the heavens. It was a living creature, covered with a smooth skin like the skin of a man.

And Karora's head lay at the root of the great *tnatantja*; he had rested thus ever from the beginning.

And Karora was thinking and wishes and desires sped through his mind. Bandicoots began to come out from his navel and from his armpits. They burst through the sod above and sprang into life.

And now dawn was beginning to break. From all quarters men saw a new light appearing: the sun itself began to rise at Ilbalintja and flooded everything with its light. Then the Gurra ancestor was minded to rise, now that the sun was mounting higher. He burst through the crust that had covered him and the great gaping hole he left behind became the Ilbalintja Soak, filled with the

51

sweet dark juice of the honeysuckle buds. The Gurra ancestor rose, feeling hungry, since magical powers had gone out from his body.

As yet he feels dazed; slowly his eyelids begin to flutter; then he opens them a little. He gropes about dazedly; he feels a moving mass of bandicoots all around him. He is now standing more firmly on his feet. He thinks; he desires. In his great hunger he seizes two young bandicoots; he cooks them some distance away, close to the spot where the sun is standing, in the white-hot soil heated by the sun. The sun's fingers alone provide him with fire and hot ashes.

His hunger satisfied, his thoughts turn towards a helpmeet. But now evening is approaching over the whole earth; the sun hides his face with a veil of hair-string, covers his body with hair-string pendants, vanishes from the sight of men. And Karora falls asleep, stretching his arms out on both sides.

The Bushmen, those little hunters whose ancestors once had possession of the greater part of South Africa but who have been decimated and driven into the wastes of Kalahari by Bantus and Europeans, tell a charming story to explain how the sun was launched into the sky. It is like the Australian tale only in the status allowed the sun. It is venerated, but certainly not divine. Indeed the Bushman legend says that the sun was an ordinary man in the days of their first ancestors, although he was not one of them. When the story begins he was an old man lying on the ground, and the light, which shone from his armpits, illuminated only the immediate neighbourhood of his hut. An old woman told 'the children' that they must go to him, wait until he fell asleep, then lift him stealthily and throw him into the sky. This they did, and while they waited the old man 'lifted up his elbow, his armpit shone upon the ground, as he lay'. Then after a while (or rather after many repetitions by the story-teller) 'they stealthily approached him, they took hold of him, they all took hold of him together, they lifted him up, they raised him while he felt hot. Then they threw him up . . . they spoke to him . . . "O Sun! Thou must altogether stand fast, thou must go along, thou must stand fast, while thou art hot.'"

The children were successful and returned to boast of it to their grandmother. After a rather obscure passage about the shining of sun and moon in which the dependence of the moon seems to be recognized, the legend ends with general rejoicing. One of the reasons given for wanting to get the sun into the sky was to 'dry the Bushman rice' (ants' eggs). This final passage expresses the emotion of the hunter at its purest.

> The Sun is here, all the earth is bright; the Sun is here, the people walk while the place is light, the earth is light; the people perceive the bushes, they see the other people; they see the meat which they are eating; they also see the springbok, they also head the springbok in summer; they also head the ostrich in summer; they are shooting the springbok in summer, while they see that the Sun shines they see the springbok; they also steal up to the gemsbok; they also steal up to the kudu, while they feel that the whole place is bright; they also visit each other, while they feel that the Sun shines, the earth also is bright, the Sun shines upon the path. They also travel in summer; they are shooting in summer; they hunt in summer; they espy the springbok in summer; they go round to head the springbok; they lie down; they feel that they lie in a little house of bushes; they scratch up the earth in the little house of bushes, they lie down while the springbok come.

On the huge, smooth rock faces of their hunting lands the Bushmen painted pictures of springbok and other game in a lively and realistic style curiously similar to some of the pictures left so long before by the Stone Age hunters in Europe. The likeness is enough to suggest that the imagination of these two groups of hunting peoples, though separated by many thousands of years, worked in very much the same way. Perhaps, then, the sun stories told by our Palaeolithic forebears had much in common with *The Children are Sent to Throw the Sleeping Sun into the Sky* both in the kind of ideas expressed and in the way of expressing them. But how much greater would have been the longing to have the sun 'stand fast in the sky' in the chill of a glaciated Europe!

About twelve thousand years ago the grip of the last glaciation began to weaken. The ice sheets which covered so much of the northern hemisphere in America, in Europe and Asia, the heavy ice caps and glaciers which crowned many mountain ranges further south, began their slow retreat. This was the fourth of the great freezes to grip the earth during the million years which saw the emergence of man from among his apelike ancestors. Each seems to have lasted between fifty and a hundred thousand years, while warm periods intervening varied more widely. What caused them? The warmth or coldness of the earth is so directly dependent upon the sun that one's thoughts turn at once in that direction. But most of the few minds capable of interpreting the sun's nature to the rest of us are agreed that no fluctuations so rapid and abrupt could take place in the amount of solar radiation. So if the ice ages were indeed caused by a reduction in light and heat, it must have been in the quantity reaching or staying with us and not in the quantity (or numbers of quanta) leaving the sun. It may be that a conjunction between a number of minor irregularities in the earth's habits caused the drops in temperature. These would have been in such things as changes in the tilt of the planet's axis, small wobbles in its orbit caused by the attraction of other planets as they pass, and very gradual shifts in the orbit as a whole. Quite a different kind of explanation would attribute the ice ages to the greenhouse effect. As it is the atmosphere, and particularly its water vapour, which conserves heat by preventing the escape of infra-red radiation, if it were thinned the temperature at the earth's surface would fall. How could it have been thinned? Possibly by the passage of our planet through meteor clouds—that is to say through clouds of particles too small to burn as shooting stars from friction with our atmosphere, yet able to condense the water vapour into rain.

54

Another suggestion is that the glaciations were in part due not to any kind of change in light and heat but to mountain building. The rearing up of great chunks of the rocky crust into lofty ranges certainly could promote the forming of glaciers, and such upheavals had occurred before the ice ages began. On the other hand as the Alps, Andes, Rockies and other ranges certainly never prostrated themselves, this theory cannot account for the warm interglacial phases.

Whatever their cause, these occasions when our planet cooled down and its whole face was transformed by the power of the ice to gouge and grind, to carry and deposit huge cargoes of soil and rock, to change sea levels, make lakes and divert rivers, are a demonstration of that haphazard and therefore unpredictable aspect of our universe which to me makes it more tolerable.

Whether or no it was because earth had at that time just emerged from a meteor cloud, there is no doubt that by 8000 B.C. the ice had withdrawn a very long way. Although it took another thousand years or more for the polar ice caps and the mountain glaciers to shrink to about their present limits, the final retreat must have been fast enough to be easily noticeable to the men who were in fact pushing their summer hunting grounds northward in its wake. So it is not impossible that some stories about the sun, some of the anxiety concerning its health and stability, might spring from long traditions of hard times.

It was now that man began to change his way of wresting a livelihood from his planet. It was to bring about a revolution in his attitude to the sun far more profound than anything that could result from the onset or retreat of an ice age. It represents a major advance in the evolution of man's relationship with nature. Whatever view is held concerning the meaning and mechanics of evolution, it can no longer be questioned that it took place, and therefore that looking from the beginning of life one can see mankind shaping along an unbroken line of living forms. We see the limbs, the nervous system and the head with so remarkable a future before it developing in the vague, half-lit under-water world; the emergence into full daylight, the warming of the blood, some millions of generations following one another among the branches and tree-tops, the lifting of the body upright which went with life back on the ground. In spite of the metamorphoses—from fish to reptile, from reptile to amphibian, from amphibian to mammal, as great as those passed in a single life-span by butterfly, moth or dragonfly, all these ancestors were alike in living off the other forms of creation which were evolving beside them. With mouths, with scaly, then furry, paws, at last with hands, food was gathered in. What was there was taken, both plant and animal. When mounting intelligence and the making of tools began man's isolation from the unity of natural life in which he had existed until then, there was, to be sure, some change. The pause to make a tool for hunting was a counterpart to the pause of conscious thought. But still there was no attempt at a god-like mastery over any part of his living environment. He used tools, cunning traps and the collaboration of individuals to take the place of claws, strength and the pack. Yet once the chase was on, it was again speed, physical skill, keenness of eye, the instinct-guided body. No slow authority, no apprehensive mastership.

Now these things were to begin. As, further north, summer by summer the ice contracted, exposing fresh land for the hunters, fishers and fowlers of these latitudes, somewhere in the warmer lands lying east of the Mediterranean men and women began to control the freedom of movement, the feeding and the breeding of certain animals which proved to be amenable, and to sow and select the seed of plants.

The story of this initiation of the farming life which was to be man's main support thereafter has been told hundreds of times. Every possible phrase to describe it has been worn to a cliché. I do not want to repeat any of them, but only to strive to understand man's changing awareness of the sun, the inevitable birth of the agricultural gods.

Even the Stone Age hunters knew imaginative desire. The splendid paintings and carvings in their caves show a desire for the animals they pursued of a kind that merged into love. The images of the Great Mother show a desire for fertility that may have merged into anxiety. But now a mingling of the old awe and desire was to be wedded to a new sense of responsibility and with it to a far greater and more lasting stress.

As far as their domestic animals were concerned, they probably felt much the same longing for abundance which the hunters had known for wild game, though intensified and made more precise by their own handling of the births, their counting of kid and lamb, calf and piglet. It was the cultivation of plants and tilling of the soil that turned men's minds in a new direction. One immediate effect was to give the Great Mother, the hunters' embodiment of female fertility, a new aspect. While her original role was only enhanced by animal breeding and still more by the fact that cultivators long for many children while hunters must often destroy their new-born, she now emerged also as an expression of the fertility of the soil, as the Earth Mother. In all the centres of earliest farming—in southwest Asia, Egypt, western India and round the Mediterranean —her image was shaped, usually more stylized now, but still showing the full hips, belly and breasts of her original manifestation among the hunters. The earliest solar symbol known to me is about six thousand years old, from the village of Ghassul in the Jordan valley, while not far away, the oldest known settled cultivators in the world, at Jericho, had shaped a statuette of the Mother Goddess at least two thousand years before. This is inevitable, for she did not have to be created in the imagination of the pioneer farmers, she had haunted the mind of man for thousands of years. Yet she did acquire an altogether new facet as Earth Mother, and as time went by this was often to be split off into an independent goddess—after the

57

bewildering fashion of deities, who for ever divide and coalesce.

Far more deeply significant than the coming of the Earth Mother was the cultivators' urge to look upwards to a source of divinity outside the planet on which they trod. It was the beginning of all the Fathers which are in Heaven.

The change from hunting to agriculture led not only to a more settled life, but also to a more measured one in the sense that actions had to be repeated regularly day by day and season by season. Little though these first cultivators knew of a spinning globe, of its tilted axis and yearly journey round the sun, they had to calculate the results. The sun's seeming voyage across the heavens was their diurnal clock, its seasonal movement the timepiece for their year. It is true that in some regions the hunters had made annual migrations, but in their passive role the timetable was determined not by them but by the wild game. Now their successors had to take the initiative in mating, sowing and reaping.

So from quite early days of farming the sun must have begun to assume what was always to be one of its leading attributes—divine power as a source of order and measurement. Often in later times this was to develop into the idea of the sun as a dispenser of divine justice. The development in part came naturally from the unity of law and order, but was also due in part to the image of the sun as an all-seeing eye which, from its high road in the sky, could detect every man's most secret deeds. While the abstract concept of justice is not likely to have troubled these tiny farming communities as slowly they forged the chains of peasant custom, the much simpler notion of the heavenly watchman may well have appealed to them as the divinity of the sun grew and brightened.

While those attributes of the sun which in fact sprang from the fixed motions of the solar system may from the first have been an important part of that waxing divinity, quite a different group, those which in fact sprang from solar energy, were probably always of greater power. To the peasant striving for a good living, order and measurement, law and the watchful eye, cannot have half the emotional appeal of the idea of fertility. As soon as man had taught himself to plant seeds in the soil and wait to harvest them he was bound to discover the power of the sun over his crops. Those who lived near forest or woodland would see how vegetation came only where the sunlight could strike through to the ground; all cultivators would have observed that crops sown in heavy shade did not flourish and would have been struck by the pallor, feebleness and early death of plants struggling to grow in near darkness. Equally almost all would become aware that the sun's warmth was needed for the germination and ripening of the grain.

So, as lord of crops and measurer of seasons, the sun was deified. No longer a minor hero in hunters' tales, it became a god to be served by ritual, prayer and sacrifice, and to be worked upon by magic.

While not universal, sun worship was to become immensely widespread. There is hardly a region of the world that did not know it at some time and in some form. What seems astonishing to a dweller in a land of cloud, rain and mist where the sun is evidently adorable, is that its worship should have prevailed equally, and indeed even more, in lands where the sun might seem a tyrant, scorching and withering all life and hope. Egypt, Persia, Mesopotamia, India, Central and South America, all these are territories where summers end with the land parched and brown and where crops can be shrivelled by drought, yet they include the very regions (other than Japan) where sun gods achieved their greatest glory. Evidently to peoples at home nearer to the equator, the sun standing straight overhead does not seem so hostile as it does to us pale northerners. They are, on the contrary, only made more aware of its majesty and power. It is also true, however, that among some of these peoples a cruel and even murderous aspect of the solar deity was recognized. But it provoked propitiation rather than loathing or neglect. It is more sad than surprising that often at the simpler levels of religious emotion it is the cruel forces—of storm, disease, death—that receive the greatest tribute. Benign powers call for less service and sacrifice.

The divinity of the sun as it rose in the minds of men was very generally seen to be masculine. This would appear so inevitable that it is astonishing to find that it is not quite so universal as the femininity of the Earth Goddess. It is not only the obvious symbolism of their physical presences. The earth which is ploughed, receives the seed and nourishes the growth of the new life; the sun which strikes down to germinate the seed, the sunbeams with their phallic suggestion. But deeper than that, it seems that the archetypal inheritance of darkness and light instilled in us since the beginning of life is in some manner linked with the sexual principles, with the yin and the yang. Carl Jung does not hesitate to identify the earth, darkness, the ocean, the unconscious, with the feminine principle, light and consciousness with the masculine. He finds, too, that in modern man the sun is the usual symbol for the individual consciousness. Girls and women feel close to nature; when their unconscious is excited into poetry (usually by love or eroticism) they write innocently of themselves as trees and flowers and earth itself. Men are inclined to feel themselves as aliens to this world, to have spirits that belong to some more lofty sphere. When raised to their highest pitch of imagined glory as divine kings, it is with the sun they most often identify themselves. And, to return to simpler things, in the beautiful little sign of the yin and the yang, formed heaven knows how deep down in time and the unconscious, the female yin has emerged as black while the male yang has the whiteness of the sun, of consciousness.

The idea could hardly be more directly and inevitably expressed than in this creation story told by the Apache Indians after they had given up their hunting life and learnt the agricultural way of life from the Pueblo. First they describe how in the beginning there was no world—'nothing but Darkness,

Water and Cyclone'—but there were the gods who had always existed and

> who had the material out of which everything was created. They made the world first, the earth, the underworld, and they made the sky. They made the earth in the form of a living woman and called her Mother. They made the sky in the form of a man and called him Father. He faces downward, and the woman faces up. He is our father and the woman is our mother.

This simple and profoundly truthful concept is at the heart of the tenaciously held faith of many of the American Indian peoples. Very often, moreover, the male deity is addressed not as Sky but as Sun Father; this confusion, this ever-shifting interchange between a universal god of the heavens and one embodied in the sun alone is common throughout the world and at all times. It is not difficult to understand. It may be said to find one of its explanations in the exalted and lovely imagery of the Pueblo, peoples who nearly achieved a high civilization, comparable to that of Maya and Inca, at the time of our early Middle Ages, and who ever since have lived a settled village life in a part of their ancient homelands.

I choose to write at some length about the Pueblo partly because they are a humble yet cultured farming people whose way of life seems to have much in common with that of the earliest farmers in the Old World, but more because, at one remove only, I am in touch with one of their sun priests, a true Koshairi. This is the only place in this book of mine in which I can claim to have had questions answered by such a priest, a man whose office makes him a master of the sun, who could, if he did not love the world, halt it in its tracks or plunge us back into endless night.

His name is Valencio and he comes from Santa Ana, a pueblo built of soft red-brown adobe on the banks of the Rio Grande. Near Santa Ana is one of the ancient pueblo of his people, one which has acquired the name of the Coronado Monument, because it was on the line of this conqueror's march. The

curator of the Monument is John Sinclair, and Valencio is his
assistant. It so happens that the chief *kiva* there, the circular
underground sacred house of the Pueblo Indians, has its wall
paintings extraordinarily well preserved. Here, in brilliant
colours, we can see the doings of the nature gods, see sun, rain
and storm depicted, all to the purpose of bringing more maize,
more universal abundance to the community. In fact these
murals illustrate the tradition which Valencio has inherited
from his ancestors, the ceremonial life which he himself enacts,
and which, I hope and pray, will be handed on to his children
and his children's children.

John Sinclair, the writer, brought up in England, has so great
a loathing of the admass way of life that he has retreated with
his wife to this ruin, isolated except in the tourist season, where
he can look across the Rio Grande, set with huge cotton trees,
to the desert and the sentinel mountains. The sun is very much
lord of this desert country, not only through its strength and
unshaded brightness but because the whole scene is transformed
by its journey. There is the bright blue morning with every
detail sharp, the mountains craggy and near, the dull, camel-
coloured afternoon and the enchanted evening hours when
desert and mountains look like a bed of petunias seen through
smoke.

I asked John Sinclair whether the Sky Father was a true Sun
God or rather an Amerind Zeus. He replied that as far as he had
been able to learn from years of talk with Valencio and the
other Koshairis, Oshatsh, the Sun, in spite of his seeming
brilliance in our eyes, serves as a shield to protect frail humanity
from the intense light of the Great Spirit, the shaper of the
universe, who travels across the sky behind him showering
blessings on the earth and the people of his creation. This concept of the sun as a shield set between man and the overwhelming creative light seems to me not only imaginatively inspired,
but one which we might all find acceptable. We know now
that our star, that gaseous ball with a nuclear furnace at its core,

was the immediate creator of all life on earth; but intuition and reason alike both make us inclined to believe that this was but a parochial creation, and that behind it lies some great source of life and mind, much as my own consciousness lies behind the hand which spells these words. I should not find it hard to worship Oshatsh.

This is the loftiest theology of the Pueblo. As with the religion of almost all peoples, it exists side by side with ideas and practices much cruder or more naïve. Generally, like other American Indians, the Pueblo regard all that is below us as feminine, all that is above as masculine. The underground *kiva*, where the men can keep their sacred masks and robes and guard the secrets of their ritual preparations out of sight of the world, is entered through an opening in the roof. The main pole of the rough ladder which leads down into the shadowy room is always left very long so that it thrusts obliquely towards the sky. Although there are other interpretations (and probably all are simultaneously true) the simplest story is that the dark cavity of the *kiva*, the opening of the hatchway and the penetrating ladder symbolize the act of coition between Sun Father and Earth Mother.

In the floor of every *kiva*, whether it is still at the heart of the religious life of a thriving village, or whether it lies gaping in one of the many ruins from which Pueblo life has receded, there is a small hole set with stones, symbolizing the entrance to Shipapu, the underworld which is also the womb of Naiya Ha'atse, the Earth Mother. In the beginning the first human beings emerged into the upper world through this opening, and so will every new-born baby to the end of time. When the Sun God descends behind the West World Mountain he enters the underworld and spends the night with such lesser deities as Iatik, the Corn Mother, who gave to mankind the maize which was, as she said, 'the very milk of my breasts'. In the morning Oshatsh is ready once more to rise up behind the East World Mountain and start his climb to the zenith.

Many sun myths are told by these Indians living by the Rio Grande. They are full of contradictions; for instance in Valencio's village of Santa Ana it is held that Iatik made the two sisters who in turn made mankind, while at Zia, which is only ten miles away and where the villagers speak the same Keres tongue, the creation of the sisters is attributed to the great Spider, Sus'istinako. It might be thought that this meant that the Spider is an alternative form of the Corn Mother, Iatik, but in fact the Zia assert that he is male, while it is the Santa Ana people who call this being the Spider Grandmother. Again, and even more baffling, when the Koshairis go into retreat for the winter solstice to work for the safe return of the sun, in one of the chants it has to be addressed as My Sun Mother, a sudden reversal of the normal Sun Father which Valencio can do nothing to explain.

One of the simplest sun myths is told at Santa Ana. In the underworld there was only darkness, so when the First People came out of Shipapu to walk on the face of the earth and found the sun burning overhead they were terrified. They tried to escape back into the underworld, and would have done so had not the Koshairis come to the rescue. They saw that the way to dispel their people's terror was to make them laugh, so they began to clown, doing all kinds of antics—mostly erotic. So the First People were filled with merriment and saw that the upper world and its sunlight were good. As for the Koshairis, many of them have continued to clown ever since. I have myself watched some of these holy clowns at the great Shalako ceremony at Zuni, and found them really funny even though I could not understand their bawdy jokes. At Santa Ana, then, they know that sex and laughter cast out fear, and free us to lead a life in the sun.

The Zia tell another quite different and more ornate story. They say that in the beginning there was no light and everyone and everything was very cold and damp and miserable. Sus'istinako decided that he must do something about it, so he spun a web of corn meal fixed to the four points of the compass, and in the north-west quadrant he placed one magic bundle, in the north-east another. Then the Spider chanted and enacted all due rites with prayer-sticks and holy water and tobacco until the two bundles began to tremble like gourd rattles shaken in a dance, and to emit small murmurs. Then the bundles burst open, and from each one stepped a woman. The sister who came from the western bundle was the Mother of the Indians, while the sister from the eastern bundle (so the story now goes) was the Mother of the White People, the Negroes and the Germans. Sus'istinako went on chanting, the two women danced and all creation emerged—animals, birds, trees, corn, melons, beans, turquoise and flint—the good things of life. But still it was quite dark; people bumped into one another and could take no pleasure in the new creation. So the Spider Sus'istinako ordered the two sisters to make the sun. They gathered up the red and the white materials that were needed —abalone, redstone and haematite. They ground them up with water and shaped the dough into a gigantic ball, then carried it towards the East World Mountain where they encamped and performed fitting ceremonies. Next they carried the ball to the top of the mountain and peered into the depths beyond, which seemed even darker than the darkness of the rest of the world. They pitched it down, but before long it began to ascend once more and to shine, faint and blue at first but turning to yellow as it stood above the people. Then a new sound was heard as men and women began to sing, delighted with one another and with the beauty of the world revealed to them by the coming of light.

Most of the Pueblo myths treat of the sun as a source of light and fertility and happiness, but the Indians also recognize the divinity of the sun as Measurer. Every day of the year the War Chief, who in some ways acts as the Headman of these most peaceful villagers, watches Oshatsh as he rises behind the eastern mountain peaks. From the point of his emergence he takes the

God's orders for all seasonal acts and the rites which prepare the way for them. So the War Chief hands on Oshatsh's commands to the people for ditching and irrigating, for planting and harvesting.

In the same way the daily stations of the sun give the signal for special acts of worship addressed to Oshatsh himself. The most important of these take place at the summer and winter solstices, the one held in May soon after the Corn Dances at the pueblo of San Felipe, the other in mid-November after the Jemez Corn Dance. The dates are puzzling. When John Sinclair asked Valencio why the solstices were celebrated a month ahead of the White Man's reckoning, and indeed ahead of the obvious solar reckoning, he could only reply, 'Because that is the way we want it.'

The recognition of the sun as Measurer, and the careful attendance on its stations, are a part of the continuous awareness of the cardinal points of the compass, and of zenith and nadir, characteristic of Pueblo and of most other Amerind cultures. Each quarter has its own colour, and this world and the under-world are seen as divided into four regions corresponding to the cardinal points. It is curious and pleasing that these Indians, who have no knowledge of actual world geography, nevertheless live with this consciousness of the world lying quartered around them. When I was watching the Shalako and the clowns dancing in a house at Zuni, I found myself sitting against the family shrine which had a path of corn meal leading up to it from the doorway; hanging just above it was an equal-armed wooden cross painted with the colours of the four quarters and with a bird set in the position of the zenith. The same figure is, of course, represented by the arms of the corn-meal web spun by Sus'istinako in the creation myth. Incidentally, one of the two great Shalako divinities had golden-rayed sunflower designs woven into his skirt, while the other had symbols for rain and clouds.

Every ritual occasion on which Oshatsh is himself honoured

has its appropriate prayer, spoken together with the appropriate act—the offering of corn meal, the planting of prayer-sticks and other more elaborate ceremonial. Each prayer is divided into a statement of the occasion, a description of the offering, and the request. The following prayer which is daily addressed to the rising Oshatsh shows that these requests are not greedy and grasping but are simply to beseech him to fulfil his divinity at its best and fullest.

> *Now this day, my Sun Father,*
> *Now that you have come out standing*
> *To your sacred place.*
>
> *That from which we draw the water of life*
> *Prayer meal—*
> *Here I give unto you.*
>
> *Your long life,*
> *Your old age,*
> *Your waters,*
> *Your seeds,*
> *Your riches,*
> *Your power,*
> *Your strong spirit,*
> *Of all these, to me may you grant.*

Here, surely, is a prayer which simple agriculturists of all times and all places might address to their Sun Father until wrong knowledge sealed hearts, minds and lips?

HEAD OF PUEBLO INDIAN KACHINA
Eagle feather headdress

SUN OF JUSTICE

THE ACHIEVEMENT OF Bronze Age civilization marked a crucial stage in the growing up of *Homo sapiens*, with all that implies for better and for worse. Now, five thousand years later, it is easy to think of the rise and fall of civilizations, but this was the first time our world had ever known one. It was the first time the globe had supported cities, palaces and temples, roadways and their traffic; the first time human society had supported artisans and masons, merchants and nobles, scribes, priests and kings. This step towards adulthood, however, was taken only in a few tiny patches on the earth's surface; over most of the rest of it mankind continued in its old ways, either with simple farming by small, self-supporting and illiterate communities, or by the hunting which had gone on since the beginning.

The change in the habits and values of life that went with living many thousands together in cities, inevitably affected man's relationship with the sun. But before describing these more general happenings, I must record one significant event of a different kind. It belongs to the series which began with the development of the first eye able to respond to daylight, and continued with the naming of the sun by the spoken word. This next event was the pegging down of that name with written symbols. Writing was first achieved in Sumeria, beginning with pictograms but rapidly evolving into the strange reed-written script of cuneiform. Among the earliest signs, it is not surprising to discover, was one for the sun. So now a man could not only speak of the sun but could send messages about it, could record something of its behaviour and movements. He could, moreover, write down and preserve for our eyes to see (in daylight which is still the same but which shines on so different a world) the myths and hymns in which the sun was exalted. From the earliest texts, the sign for this sun was always accompanied by a determinative meaning divinity.

Existence in a large community where men were brought together as much by where their houses stood as by their tribal or kinship ties, inevitably led to a weakening of custom and a strengthening of conscious order and law. For the individual, civil order, wider horizons, knowledge of foreign peoples, led to a heightening of personal self-consciousness and of intellect at the expense of intuition. All these trends encouraged a higher theology, a greater awareness of order in the cosmos and particularly of the heavenly bodies, with which the order of civilization could be identified. Yet at the same time men still thought in terms of myth and not of logic, and the gods remained wholly immanent in nature. Thus the whole tremendous force of pristine civilization went into establishing harmony between man, nature and divinity, or, as it could be more simply expressed, between heaven and earth. And as the greatest of the heavenly bodies, the sun came to live in the heart of society.

Yet in another sense the sun and all divinities became more remote from the ordinary man and woman. This, and many of the other changes, were brought about by the growth of a professional priesthood. I have called Valencio of Santa Ana a sun priest, and so he is, but he and his fellow Koshairis are very much part-time priests. Valencio himself helps to look after the Coronado Monument, most of his fellows look after their maize and sheep and cattle; it is only on special occasions, such as the retreat before the solstice, that they can expect the community to support them. In the pueblos, and doubtless also in the Neolithic villages of the Old World, the priests had to grow their grain and meat, while all the villagers enacted the rites and sacred dances of the passing seasons and personified the gods when they appeared upon earth. In the cities which grew up beside Tigris and Euphrates, Nile and Indus, the responsibility for intercession with the gods became so evidently onerous that it required the complete devotion of many priests. So the initiated and professional go-between was instituted, the regular priesthood able to interpret man's wishes to the gods and the gods' intentions to man. The priesthoods which started with every man's support, but which too often ended in exploitation and abuse.

So as villagers became citizens they no longer themselves enacted the rites which made the sun rise in the morning and which turned it safely back at dead of winter; they became instead a congregation. Nor could a professional priesthood of growing power be satisfied to worship the gods in the village squares, alleys and houses, or at the springs, lakes and mountains linked with them in simple myth. The god must have his own house, a richly furnished house, where, moreover, a line must be drawn beyond which the ordinary citizen might not pass, a line cutting off the Holy of Holies where only the foot of a priest could safely tread. So at the heart of every one of the new cities, temples were built on a scale to dwarf the clustering houses of the mortal inhabitants.

Only one other building might rival the god's dwelling, or even be a part of it, and that was the house of the king. For another institution of Bronze Age civilization of prime significance in this history was that of kingship. Here was a go-between whose relationship with his people and with the gods was more direct and potent than that of the ordinary ministering priest. For kings embodied the divine in their own persons even though the order of their divinity varied widely. In Egypt where a mystical chieftainship went back to remote times, it was a natural development that an absolute monarch should govern the land when it became united. So it was that from the beginning of the Old Kingdom Pharaoh was himself a god, a full member of the pantheon. In Mesopotamia, on the other hand, where from the first the city state was the political unit and where government was by council of the citizens, kings were appointed as governors when the strains and responsibilities of high civilization became too much for the old democratic ways. Days when there were no kings were traditionally remembered. It is not surprising, therefore, that with few exceptions the rulers of the Sumerian and Akkadian cities made no claim to godhead. One of their most usual titles meant 'Great Man'. They embodied the sovereign power of the people, and kingship had 'come down to them from heaven', yet the men themselves were no more than mortal. Some trace of royal divinity survives, one of the many strange anomalies in our scientific age, even in the constitutional monarchies of western Europe, though it is left but the merest crack between the social, political and mass entertainment aspects of their sovereignty.

There has been a powerful tendency for sun gods to be identified with divine kings even in nations where they were not the supreme deities of their pantheons. This is clearly, albeit corruptly, expressed in the attitudinizing of that most Christian monarch Louis XIV as *Le Roi Soleil*. The majesty of the supreme head, of the personification of his society, is identified by the psyche with light, with brilliance; this, I think, is one cause of the tendency. Then it is an all but universally recognized attribute of the inspired person to have bright-shining eyes (Beware! Beware! His flashing eyes, his floating hair!), and the interplay between eye and sun, sun and eye, is one of the unbroken threads in solar myth and imagery. Finally, and this was surely of the greatest importance throughout the Ancient World, a heightened sense of order and organization which was a part of the new ways of civilization found its centre point in kingship. The Sun God was the measurer and all-seeing dispenser of justice, the king the very pivot of the law and right ordering of society. It was a part of the total inter-penetration of man, nature and divinity.

More precisely, too, it seems that in Mesopotamia, and in a rather different manner in Egypt, the regular and coherent movement of sun, moon and planets having been discovered after patient study by generations of priests, the earthly polity of city, state or nation was seen as striving to reflect or repro-duce this harmony of the heavens. And as, possibly below some remotely exalted deity of the sky, the Sun God was the evident master of the heavenly order, so the king, his earthly counter-part, was gladly recognized as his agent or true incarnation. So began the history of sun kings which can be pursued from Mesopotamia and Egypt to Ancient Mexico and Peru and on to Japan, until, at last, a half-obscured glint of it appears in that golden robe in which Elizabeth II of England was secretly vested (hidden by the canopy even from the eye of the tele-vision camera) at her coronation in Westminster Abbey. Per-haps it lingered, too, in the words of Archbishop Fisher, himself a priest hardly likely to have much sympathetic under-standing of sun worship, when before the enthronement of the Queen he prayed that God might establish the throne in righteousness that 'it may stand fast for evermore, like as the sun before her, and as the faithful witness in heaven'.

It is a remarkable coincidence that a discovery and an inven-tion attendant on the creation of Bronze Age civilization came just in time to provide symbols for the sun gods and their temples. These were gold and the wheel. Gold was the first metal to be worked by man and was already in use between five and six thousand years ago. Its colour and bright sheen, and above all the fact that it was eternally bright, incorruptible and untarnished, meant that it was instantly recognized as the metal of the sun. Through all the history of civilization gold remained as it were the solar garb, dressing heaven knows how many solar disks (of which the one raised by the Incas in their great temple at Cuzco is only the most famous), kings and queens, images and crowns, haloes and hosts of other solar forms.

The invention of the wheel was a necessary part of the growth of city life. Better transport than the sledge, travois or pannier was needed for the long-distance trade and the food markets which were a part of the new ways. The earliest wheels were of the solid wooden kind known to have been in use by the middle of the fourth millennium B.C. in Mesopotamia, and still to be seen in many lands turning side by side with those of the latest motor-car. Although these do not evoke the idea of the sun so immediately as the spoked wheel, which may not have been devised much before 2000 B.C., the image of a travelling disk was probably already enough to suggest it. Furthermore some solid wheels had the felloes held with radiate clamps in a way which was as suggestive of rays as spokes themselves. The identification would have been reinforced by notions concerning solar transport. All peoples were impressed by the Sun God's tremendous journey across the sky and wished to think of him using the best vehicle available. It was only in times and lands where there were no carts, boats or riding animals that he was allowed to walk. In the earliest Sumerian texts he is still on foot, but as soon as it was available on earth he was supplied with a carriage, and this idea became widespread. So that quite apart from the identification of the wheel with the sun disk, there was early an association of the two. Curiously, the same thing can be said of the wheel and royalty. The oldest surviving wheeled vehicles are hearses, buried together with slaughtered draught animals and servants, in royal graves at Kish, Susa and Ur. Gordon Childe observed 'Before 2500 B.C. burial with a hearse had become a prerogative of kings in Mesopotamia. Significantly enough the first wheeled vehicles to survive in Georgia, south Russia, Bohemia and Bavaria are also hearses, buried in the tombs of barbarian kings

73

or chiefs. It looks as if the association of wheeled vehicles and kingship had been diffused with the wheel itself.' So, although it is by no means universally consistent, we seem to see a glittering cavalcade of kings, gold-clad and crowned, of sun gods and flickering wheels driving along the routes of heaven and of earth.

As man civilized himself for the first time in history, then, his relationship with the sun and sky certainly became more exalted and more consciously organized. Divine kings might mean that the Sun God or at least his regent was present on earth. Priests studied the heavens, learnt more of the movements of the heavenly bodies and saw the heavenly order as interwoven with the human and terrestrial. So far, indeed, did the leaders of society begin to look upward that Mother Earth below their feet received less honour. The Great Goddess, who had been the first and for so long the sole religious image to be conceived and given material expression among mankind, came to take second place to sky deities in most centres of Bronze Age civilization. This had the further meaning that in a much profounder sense the masculine principle gained a new dominance over the feminine—which had perhaps achieved its greatest dignity during the millennia of village agriculture.

History moves on through time. It is made up of events in the outer world—the development of agriculture and of cities, the institution of sovereignty, the discovery of gold, the invention of the wheel. But at the same time it in part represents the happenings in the inner world of men's minds, the psychological history of mankind. Again to some extent the psychological growth of the individual repeats that of the species, just as does his bodily growth. No genius could be great enough to disengage the intricate plaiting of these three strands, their causes and effects. All that can be attempted is always to keep them in mind, so that when one strand is being examined, the presence of the others is never forgotten. At this period of time, the fourth and third millennia B.C., it is possible to see the rise of the citizen above the villager and hunter as a heightening of self-consciousness at the expense of the unconscious. The city broke down the organic life of the tribe, the individual was forced to become more aware of himself and his separateness. Light and the masculine advanced in relation to dark and the feminine. The cause of the religious change can be seen as the law and order of a more complex society under authoritarian rule, the institution of a professional priesthood with the resulting development of astronomy and theology, but it can also be seen to be the psychological growth of man. Deities can be accepted quite simply as personifications of the powers of nature in the outer world, but they can also be seen as the manifestation of the inner forms of the psyche. Both interpretations are true, for the impressions made upon us by the outer world and the expressions of our inner life must always flow into one another, enhance and reflect one another. Nevertheless there can be no doubt that the human psyche is the dynamic force within our history. If an appropriate analogy is sought, it could be found in that nuclear furnace of hydrogen and helium within the sun. Invisible and unknowable, the whole solar system yet depends upon it, from Mercury to Pluto and from the crown in the Tower to the icy rings of Saturn.

Returning now to the river valleys with their fertile land chequered by irrigation ditches below the naked sun, because the earliest farming villages had grown up in the hilly country surrounding the Tigris-Euphrates valley, Mesopotamia had a slight lead over Egypt in the making of civilization. Yet although this was so, and although Egypt probably took over a number of ideas, such as writing, from the pioneers, the two lands developed strongly individual ways of life, and quite different interpretations of man's fate. In Egypt the unbroken fertility of the valley floor, walled in and protected from invasion by desert, encouraged the creation of a unified kingdom; the extraordinary regularity of the annual flood, a view of life as essentially orderly and stable. No wonder, then, that the sun, the high and unchanging regulator of the seasons, there became supreme.

In contrast the huge and ill-defined flood plain of the Tigris and Euphrates had little to give it unity. It was open to attack from several sides, while the irregularity of the floods, coming at no fixed time and sometimes scanty, sometimes overwhelmingly destructive, impressed the Sumerians and their successors with the harsh incalculability of the human condition. When I went to Iraq, I thought it one of the drearest and most heartless lands I had ever seen. The dead-flat, baked expanse of the plain, the monotonous colouring which seemed to range only from light khaki to dark, and, most depressing of all, the dreary veil of dust over everything, the heavy-handed heat, made me marvel that its inhabitants could ever have been energetic and brilliantly original, among the greatest innovators of history.

The Sumerians and Akkadians, faced by such harsh and incalculable conditions, while esteeming good order, nevertheless did not, like the Egyptians, take it as part of the scheme of things, but saw existence as an endless struggle against chaos. And they saw mankind as being condemned to everlasting slavery to the gods. In the Babylonian *Epic of Creation*, Marduk, having created man, is made to say 'Let him be burdened with the toil of the gods that they may freely breathe.'

Thus when civilization flowered, not in a single kingdom as in Egypt but in a number of rival city states, it is not surprising that each was recognized as being the absolute property of a divinity. In the beginning, perhaps, the temple of the presiding god or goddess was the only one, but soon, as populations mounted, temples to other gods were set up, though always under the domination of the city god and his mortal stewards. Every citizen belonged to a temple community, and all of them, from peasant, herdsman, carpenter and gardener up to the officials, merchants and priests were known as 'the people of the god Marduk' (or whoever the deity might be). Each community, with its 'god's house' and its lands, was organized very much like a medieval English manor, with the god as the lord and the people labouring in his service. A proportion of the land, known as the 'fields of the god', was cultivated communally for the temple, the produce being used for sacrifices, for the support of temple workers, and to be issued to the community in times of special hardship. The remainder of the land was leased by the god, in exchange for a tithe of the produce, as allotments for private cultivation.

The chief priest of the city god's temple, which, with its lofty Ziggurat serving as a kind of stairway between earth and heaven, usually towered above the town, might very often be the king or governor of the whole state. When government by council of elders gave way to personal rule, the change was theologically justified by the principle of divine election. The kingship was not accepted as being either permanent or hereditary. In theory each ruler was appointed by the gods. In some cities, however, and notably in Erech, a permanent monarchy was more or less firmly established. Foreshadowing on a vaster scale what was later to happen in Greece, the city states struggled against one another, and often one city, personified in the god and his steward, the king, established a hegemony over the rest. After the time of Sargon, towards the end of the third millennium B.C., the paramount king might impose his full authority over the whole of Mesopotamia and its empire, and force the states to unite in the face of common enemies.

This curious social system of theocratic communism in large numbers of small states led to a complex and shifting theology which was only further complicated by movement of the centre of power among the peoples and regions of the Two Rivers. When urban life was coming into being during the fourth and early third millennia B.C. the pioneers were the Sumerians, a non-Semitic people living in the extreme south of the valley where Ur, Uruk (Erech) and Isin had their turn as leading cities. In the centre of the valley lived the Semites often known as Akkadians, who, having absorbed much of Sumerian culture, became dominant in Mesopotamia from the time of Sargon, king of the city state of Akkad. A few centuries later, at the opening of the second millennium, Hammurabi, King of Babylon, a great conqueror, administrator and codifier of the laws, made his city one of the chief centres of power and culture of the ancient world. Power then shifted north once again to another Semitic people, the Assyrians, dwelling in the great mountain-girt upper basin where Assur, Nimrud and Nineveh were all in their day capital cities of the Assyrian Empire. Yet the whole land maintained a cultural and religious cohesion, which meant that the gods of one people would be identified with those of another, as later the Roman pantheon was to be identified with the Greek. At the same time in each city state the city god was likely to be equated with the supreme deity of the country as a whole, and even, when the city state became paramount, virtually to take his place.

Where in this divine kaleidoscope did the Sun God appear? In early Sumeria he occupied a relatively small corner of the pattern of the national theology, but later, with the growing power of kings and the shift of power towards the Semitic peoples, his golden presence filled a larger and larger part. In Egypt, as will appear, the original generative source of life was seen to be male, but in Mesopotamia it was female—the universe was conceived rather than begotten. Tiamat, primeval chaos, was 'mother of the deep who fashions all things'. Thus, in contrast with Egypt, a male Sun God was bound, theologically, to take a secondary place in the pantheon.

In the original Sumerian theology, which was never allowed to die, Anu the Sky God (who had his main seat of worship at Uruk), Enlil of the city of Nippur, god of air and storm, and Enki, the wise god of the waters whose shrine was at Eridu, formed the supreme trinity with Ninhursag, one of the many manifestations of the ancient Mother Goddess, making a fourth among the great, creative divinities. Anu was the king of the gods, but, as was often to happen again to remotely exalted sky

78

gods, he seems to have drifted above all power—like a British Member of Parliament being raised to a seat in the Lords. He was largely displaced by Enlil, who in the early theology, having defeated Tiamat and the other powers of chaos, created mankind by striking the ground with his pickaxe, enabling the first human beings to break through and begin their toil for the gods. Enlil remained a supreme national divinity even when Semitic divinities of Babylonia and Assyria had, as his deputies, taken over most of his attributes and functions, including the creation of man.

It was in a secondary trinity below these creator gods that the Sun God took his place in the Sumerian theology. First of these was Nanna, the Moon, city god of Ur, who was Enlil's son, perhaps because the Sumerians felt that this silvery and inconstant being must have been created out of air. Utu, the Sun God, was his child, as was the third of the Trinity, Inanna, goddess of the planet Venus and of love and fertility. Nanna's superior position as father of the Sun God (an exceptional form of the relationship between sun and moon) was probably due to the early pre-eminence of his city of Ur. Utu was also known to the Sumerians as Babbar, and his temple as E-babbara— House of the Sun.

From the first, Semitic deities were recognized as counterparts to the Sumerian; thus Sin was the Semitic Nanna, Ishtar was Inanna, while the Semitic Sun God was Shamash. After the days of Hammurabi, Marduk, the city god of Babylon nominally still acting as Enlil's deputy, became for most people the supreme creator god. This, as will appear, is of much significance for the present theme, as evidently the Semites of the Two Rivers had an ancient tradition for solar worship which was not lost in Marduk.

If one accepts a pantheon quite simply as representing human reactions to the powers of nature as they are encountered in the outer world, then one can say that in Sumeria, the lower valley of the Tigris-Euphrates, where the marvellously fertile silt had recently been reclaimed from marsh and swamp, life evidently came from the earth, while the sun, beating down without mercy and finally in high summer burning all vegetation and making human life miserable, could not be conceived as having any share in creation and fertility. Certainly it was the Sun God's other aspect, that of measurer and law-giver, which was at first given honour. Utu-Shamash was god of justice—which as civilization matured came more and more to be identified with righteousness. It was probably for this reason that Shamash had special powers over devils and witches, including those responsible for sickness, and that one of his titles was Shepherd of the Land. Because of his own tireless journeying, he seems also to have been a protective deity for all travellers. A Babylonian hymn to the setting sun gives expression to these ideas.

> *Oh Shamash, when thou enterest into the midst of heaven,*
> *The gate bolt of the bright heavens shall give thee greeting,*
> *The doors of heaven shall bless thee . . .*
> *And Ai thy beloved wife shall come joyfully into thy presence,*
> *And shall give rest to thy heart.*
> *A feast for thy godhead shall be spread for thee.*
> *O valiant hero, Shamash, mankind shall glorify thee.*
> *O lord of E-babbara, the course of thy path shall be straight.*
> *Go forward on the road which is a sure foundation for thee.*
> *O Shamash, thou art the judge of the world, thou directest the*
> *   decisions thereof.*

Again, in the epilogue to his famous code of laws, King Hammurabi hails Shamash as 'the great judge of Heaven and Earth', while the stela shows the king standing in adoration before the god, who is enthroned, and investing him with the ring and staff of a law-giver. At Ur, where King Ur Engur established justice 'according to the just laws of the Sun God', it was declared that Shamash punished the corrupt judge who took bribes and oppressed the people.

Even though the people of the Two Rivers could not in

III. STELA OF KING NABUPALIDDINA OF BABYLON

early time worship the Sun God as a creator, it is plain enough that his aspect as the universal judge already brought him high honour. But this was his position in what may be called the national theology—the theology pieced together and made to express a more or less coherent world view by professional priesthoods. It must also be estimated from the local point of view of the city states. Utu-Shamash was never the city god of a paramount city; had he been, no doubt like Marduk and others he would have been the accepted deputy of Enlil for the country as a whole. But he was the owning divinity of Larsa in the south and of Sippar further north, where his temple was on the east bank of the Euphrates. The citizens of these two states, then, belonged absolutely to the Sun God, worked his fields, stocked his temple and worshipped him as their supreme deity who for them assumed the functions of Enlil. Although they did not, like the Egyptians, have the Sun God present in their midst, it is doubtful if any human beings ever came closer to him than the citizens of Larsa and Sippar who accepted themselves as his absolute property as surely as a negro slave belonged to his white master.

One of the functions in the religious life of every city in the valley of the Two Rivers which the city god would fulfil as deputy for the supreme gods of the national pantheon, was in the celebration of the New Year Festival. Sometimes this was held in the early spring when young green life was being re-born, sometimes in the autumn when men were desperate after the scorching summer, when 'the force that through the green fuse drives the flower' seemed dead and all longed for its resurrection. They were as much the foremost festivals of the year as are Christmas and Easter in Christian lands. Indeed it is plain that in their celebration of the death and rebirth of the god, they are their close counterpart. So similar was the per-formance of the divine drama in Mesopotamian cities to the celebration of the passion of Christ that, when this truth was becoming apparent, Professor A. H. Sayce wrote to *The Times* saying that he believed that God had sent it as a prophecy to prepare the way for Christ. I shall return to this in its proper place.

These New Year festivals involve an aspect of the Earth Mother which I might have considered when describing her emergence from the Great Mother of the hunters. I judged, however, that the ideas expressed in the drama were not yet fully realized in the minds of the Stone Age villagers. It is a drama infinitely subtle and varied, yet always familiar, a drama in which the principle characters have very many different names yet always play much the same parts. These are the Earth Goddess and the beautiful young god who was usually both her son, because the new life had to spring from her, and her beloved mate who begot the new life. The festivals celebrate the death of the young god, with goddess and people all bewailing him, and his return to life, often accompanied by the ritual coupling of the king and queen or priestess representing the two divinities, when goddess and people rejoice. In lands near the equator the festival will be connected with the parching of all vegetation in the summer, while in colder climates it is more likely to be associated with winter death, and hence directly with the return of the sun.

In the original Sumerian form of the drama the young god was Dumuzi, or Tammuz, the creative power of spring, while the goddess was usually Inanna, the fertility of nature. Over four thousand years ago, when Ur had fallen and the city state of Isin was the foremost in the south, there are records of simple springtime cult festivals in which the marriage of these two divinities was enacted by the king, Idin-Dagan, at that time the paramount ruler of the land, and a priestess. The hymn describes how in a bedchamber in the temple:

> *A couch has been set up for my lady*
> *Grass and plants . . . cedar they purify there,*
> *Put it for my queen on that couch . . .*
> *A blanket delighting the heart, to make the bed good.*

It continues with an account of their purification and their coition, then the couple, king and priestess or god and goddess, leave the bedchamber and:

> *Around the shoulders of his beloved bride he has laid his arm*
> *Around the shoulders of pure Inanna he has laid his arm.*
> *Like daylight she ascends the throne on the great throne dais;*
> *The king, like unto the sun, sits beside her.*

So, with the marriage consummated on earth and among the gods, the couple feast and in Isin 'The people are passing the day in abundance'. The corn would soon sprout again, and cattle and sheep be led out into green fields. But in the full New Year festivals of Mesopotamia the drama was heightened and elaborated by enacting at the same time the battle of creation, the defeat of Tiamat, chaos, by the creator god and the division of her body to make heaven and earth. This great ritual brought reassurance to the people of the Two Rivers in their constant fear that human existence and civilized order would be overthrown and chaos return.

The best text describing this divine drama comes from Babylon at a time when she was capital of the empire and her god Marduk was the accepted creator god and deputy for Enlil. After a few days devoted to rites of purification, there comes the Day of Atonement. The god is "dead" or held prisoner in the underworld, symbolized by the noble mass of the Ziggurat of his temple, which at one and the same time represents the earth and its union with heaven, and the 'place of sunrise'. While the citizens crowd the narrow streets and gather round the temples in a mounting frenzy expressive of their search for the suffering god, their king has to undergo a strange rite of debasement and abdication at the hands of his chief priest in the temple of Marduk. The priest comes to him from the Holy of Holies where the statue of the god is lodged, strikes him on the face and deprives him of all the royal insignia. Then the king kneels and makes a humble declaration:

I have not sinned, O lord of the lands,
I have not been negligent regarding thy divinity
I have not destroyed Babylon . . .

Then the high priest declares that Marduk has accepted the king's words, returns the insignia, and deals another blow on the royal face, heavy enough to draw tears. The monarch has atoned, and his divine election has been renewed, as the year itself is soon to be.

The next day we can picture some part of the excited crowds streaming down to the banks of the Euphrates to watch richly decked barges coming slowly to the quays, bringing as their chief passengers visiting gods and goddesses from neighbouring cities, from Nippur and Erech, from Cutha and Kish. Probably a procession is formed to carry the deities up to the temple of Marduk where a special shrine awaits Nabu, Marduk's son and liberator. During the following days the drama builds to its climax. To the accompaniment of hymns and miming, Nabu liberates his father from the mountain and all the gods gather in council to give Marduk their strength in the coming struggle with Tiamat and the forces of chaos. The greatest procession of all builds up, and it is a procession in the likeness of an army, for Marduk is going into battle as the creator, the champion of order on heaven and earth. The throng with the king at its head pushes northward through Babylon, out through the Ishtar gate and across the broad river by boats. Now they reach the festival hall where Marduk's victory over Tiamat, over chaos, non-being and the unconscious, is perhaps enacted, certainly celebrated. Another night passes, there is a feast in the hall and the whole populace gives itself over to rejoicing; the god has been set free from the nether world, death has been defeated, creative light and order have once again triumphed over darkness and chaos. That night the marriage of god and goddess is celebrated, sometimes perhaps only by the divinities themselves in a ritual bedchamber, sometimes by the king and

84

his bride on a couch at the summit of the Zuggurat, a fitting place for the union of heaven and earth.

I have described the Babylonian New Year festival in some detail, partly because it helps to bring life to these long-buried cities where the ways of gods and men were so closely interwoven. But partly I have described it because certain illustrations of the myths which were re-enacted in these rituals show how much greater a part the Sun God played in them than might otherwise appear. These are the vigorous little scenes which Akkadian gem-cutters incised with such brilliance on cylinder seals, most of them belonging to the third millennium B.C. All show a heavily bearded god, in at least one instance undoubtedly Marduk himself, being liberated either from the mountain or from Tiamat, and all show him with sun rays rising from his shoulders. (The likeness to the Bushman portrayals of the Sun Man is remarkable.) On one of the seals the rayed deity seems to be both emerging from the mountain and flinging open the gates of the sun.

Marduk was probably originally a solar deity, taking over his other powers and functions as a supreme creator god only when Babylon wished to assimilate the ancient Sumerian pantheon. He seems to have been in particular a god of the spring sun, which would have encouraged his merger with Tammuz in the New Year festivals. This in turn led to a strengthening of the creative and fertility aspect of solar divinity in relation to the ordering and law-giving aspect first embodied in Shamash.

Indeed Tammuz seems to have become more and more often identified with Shamash himself. Most significantly, a tradition found in cuneiform texts from Sumerian down to Assyrian times was that Tammuz and Shamash dwelt together in the shade of the sacred tree of the underworld—Shamash here being seen in his night or winter aspect so readily identifiable with the dying vegetation spirit. The two gods also shared the deep shade of a sacred grove at Eridu. The natural tendency to equate the sun's daily, and vegetation's yearly, death and resurrection was one prime cause of the assimilation of the two deities, and once it had been accepted the more powerful Sun God was bound to dominate the young spirit of vegetation.

The rise of the Sun God in particular and of the solar aspect of deity in general was also helped by the growing power of kingship in Mesopotamia as the land was unified under paramount rulers and turned to imperial conquest. The bond between king and sun has already been made plain. Hammurabi himself proclaims 'I am the Sun of Babylon which causes light to rise over the land of Sumer and Akkad', and it was a usual thing for any Mesopotamian king to be given the title of "the sun of his land', while Assyrian monarchs, conquerors of a wide empire, were promoted to 'sun of the totality of mankind'.

It is not surprising, then, to find that when ascendancy in the land of the Two Rivers passed yet further northward to Assyria, the solar power rose to its full glory. Assur, the city god of the first capital of Assyria and the special protector of the royal house, was an unequivocal Sun God, and when, like Marduk before him, he took over the functions and attributes of the gods of the subjected states, this original aspect was not dimmed. His symbol was the winged solar disk and he was often pictured as an eagle. At Nimrud, a later capital of the Assyrian Empire, I have seen the excavation of ivory couch ends exquisitely carved in low relief with figures of heroes, kings and divinities. Above them all was a huge winged disk which would have spread above the royal or noble occupant of the couch just as at that time Assur himself spread his wings over all the peoples of the Two Rivers. Indeed, Assyria approached what might be called a many-faceted monotheism, so nearly had Assur absorbed all other deities into himself.

While the element of the lord of righteousness which had already been present in Shamash was strengthened so far as the Assyrians themselves were concerned, Assur turned quite a

different face to his enemies. As god of a martial people, he had
to become in part a martial god; he was, indeed, given the title
of The Warrior, and a man with a bow was often drawn beside
the symbol of the solar disk.

The Assyrian Empire was overthrown late in the seventh
century B.C., but even then the dominance of the Sun God was
not greatly weakened when Nebuchadnezzar II gave Babylon
a brilliant if brief return to power. Both he and his successor
Nabonidus spent great sums of gold on restoring and endowing
the ancient temple of the sun at Sippar, the original home of
Shamash. It was unavailing. After this last flare of greatness the
Persians under Cyrus defeated the Babylonians and Nabonidus
was taken captive. No
other event so poignantly
represents the fall of the
Ancient World of Bronze
Age civilization — and
with it the ancient gods.

THE SUN AS ALL-SEEING EYE
Jakob Boehme's *Seraphinisch
Blumengärtlein*, 1700

SUN ROYAL

THE NILE CUT its mighty groove through what was to become utter desert; it spread the floor with soil brought from the mountains, and men turned that floor into a green carpet of fertility, a carpet stretched for over a thousand miles. Most men passed all the days of their life on this green strip at the bottom of the groove, and every day of their lives, the sun soared across it from desert to desert. Its power and glory were manifest. It was plain, too, that its rays striking down upon the fields raised the wheat and the grass upon which men and their cattle and all other life depended.

Thus while the immensely rich, many-sided and imaginative religion of the Egyptians was concerned with these three powers—of the earth, of animals and of the sun—it was the heavenly power which was supreme. From very early times the sun was worshipped in Egypt, but when about five thousand years ago the whole land became united under the Pharaohs, the Sun God assumed so glorious a sovereignty that it is doubtful whether man's relationship with the star was ever more exalted than there in the Nile valley. And during that strange, brilliant, obsessive reign of Akhenaten for the only time in all history he was worshipped, and passionately, as the one true god, sole deity of all mankind.

I have followed the growing might of the Sun God in

Mesopotamia, because that was the scene of the earliest civilization and because the very fact that he was not there immediately pre-eminent but rose with kingship, unified rule and the mounting sense of justice and righteousness 'on earth as it is in heaven', makes it perhaps easier to distinguish his qualities and powers. Yet it is a relief to turn to Egypt, the land which followed Mesopotamia so nearly along the way to civilization, for by the Nile there is no need to piece together a god of justice here, with a city god there and a surviving solar deity somewhere else before the Sun God begins to shine with his true brightness. In Egypt he blazes out from the first, and seems to have ruled in the hearts and minds of the people even as the sun itself presided over their days.

Not that his worship was simple or logically coherent, except when hammered into unity by Akhenaten. It was endlessly diverse and logically contradictory. This came partly from the differing theologies constructed by different priestly schools—at Memphis, at Heliopolis, at Thebes—from wide differences between the outlook of priests and of the common people and from the influence of ancient and local gods who kept something of their identity up and down the long land of Egypt. But chiefly it came from seeking to illuminate the truth from many different directions at once, getting the most from all aspects of the sun and from the potent symbolism of its rising and setting, its seasonal rhythm. It is a little as though we, with our present knowledge, worshipped not only the different aspects of the star—the nuclear heart, the helium and hydrogen, the radiant heat and light—but also the sun as a symbol of the wholeness of the universe, of the light of intellect, of the power of science over ignorance. There were as many ingredients in the Egyptian worship of the sun as there are wavelengths in the solar radiation, and like them they combined to produce warmth and illumination.

So the Sun God was one, yet had many titles and many meanings. First and greatest he was Re, creator of the universe

89

and original king of Egypt, a supreme deity who could be identified with all others, for all came from him. It was Re who lifted the first patch of land, the Primeval Hill, out of Nun, the watery abyss, and so made it the place of first sunrise, the coming of light. He was Atum, divinity of the temple of Heliopolis, also a creator god and absolutely identified with Re after the triumph of the Heliopolitan priesthood and its theology. He was Khepri, the beetle, He Who Comes Forth, a title which expresses his self-creation as the scarab beetle was supposed to create itself out of the ball of dung in which it rolled its egg. The beetle pushing the ball of the sun up the sky became one of the most potent of all solar symbols. He was Aten, the sun's disk or orb, the physical power and being of the star. He was Harakhte, the Falcon, who was the ancient sky god Horus as manifest in the sun, and sometimes called Horus of the Horizon, or Horus of the Sunrise. Horus himself had many forms—above the rest he was Horus the Great God, the Lord of Heaven, son of Hathor the Mother Goddess, and at the same time Horus the son of Isis and Osiris, who at the cost of an eye avenged his father's murder on Seth and so became the universal symbol for filial piety, just as his eye became the symbol for all sacrifice.

Finally the Sun God was Pharaoh. For the mighty ruler of the whole land, he who wore the double crown of Upper and Lower Egypt, was himself a god. Here was no question of the god's regent or steward, of a man appointed by the gods to rule. He was divinity incarnate. Every man throughout Egypt who saluted the sunrise with prayer was also saluting his divine king, who at that moment, having been purified and revivified by his priests in the House of Morning, was climbing the stairs of the great window to salute his other self, the sun. To this all-important idea of the sun as regnant on the throne of Egypt I shall return when it is time to consider the historical changes in solar worship. For even in a land where the maintenance of an unchanging order was the ideal, the kingship was a political and personal institution as well as a religious one and so was subject to historical change.

In all his aspects, then, the Sun God was supreme in the valley of the Nile. No one visiting the ruins of his ancient kingdom can forget this for a moment. His supremacy is proclaimed by those noble symbols of his, the pyramid and obelisk. It is proclaimed by the trim falcon which perches before so many temples, stands guard over statues, spreads its wings above the doorways of temples and of tombs. It is proclaimed by the disk set between the horns of Hathor and of Isis, crowning the sun-worshipping baboon, by the disk which, as one wanders through the petrified forest of some hypostyle hall, catches the eye again and again from the huge stone columns where its incisive outline is sharpened by the light and shade flung down by the star itself. As to the means by which the Sun God made his great diurnal journey across the sky, no people among all his worshippers had a greater variety of ideas than the Egyptians, or illustrated them more charmingly. Because for them the Nile was the main thoroughfare, carrying not only the merchants and their merchandise, but also, on occasion, the sun king himself, it was inevitable that Re was most often seen to sail the heavens in a boat. The barque was depicted with high, gracefully-curved bow and stern posts, sometimes ending in lotus flowers. The Sun God may appear in it as Re in human forms, as Harakhte the sun-crowned falcon or as Khepri the beetle. In some paintings symbolic of the holy moment of sunrise, a man representing the primeval waters is lifting up the sun barque, while from a platform amidships a fat and finely naturalistic beetle is lifting the disk into the arms of Nut, the sky goddess—a double symbol of the sun's rising.

Other passengers in the Sun God's barque vary with time and place. Strangely, although he is the eternal enemy of Horus, Seth is often among them, because in one account of their struggle, when Horus had defeated him, Seth was turned into the god of storms and given a place in the boat. Certainly in their hearts not only Pharaoh but all men hoped to attain the final beatitude of being taken on board and sailing with the great god in eternal light.

Although when the notion of the barque was first conceived it must surely have been imagined as floating on the blue spaces of heaven as man-built boats floated on the waters of the Nile, the Egyptians found no difficulty in combining it with other, quite different, images. Thus when the heavens were seen as the Goddess Nut with her attenuated body arched over the world, the Sun God was shown sailing his boat along her thigh or side or above her back. Or when, instead, the sky was seen as Hathor, the Mother Goddess, in the shape of a cow straddling the world between her legs, then the barque might be shown crossing her hairy, yet star-sown, flanks.

Through all Egyptian history the Sun God made his great journey by boat, but always side by side with this image the Egyptians also saw the sun as flying with the wings of a bird. The bird was the divine falcon, Horus, especially in his manifestation as Harakhte. He might be seen in what was perhaps his most ancient form as whistling across the heavens with his shining eyes, the left one the moon, the right the sun. Again sometimes his wings were the pinions of the sky, covering the world with a feathered vault, while as Harakhte he was the sun itself, wearing the sun disk on his head as as plendid crest. In later time these two conceptions merged into the image of the winged disk in which the sun, fronted by the uraeus-cobra of the Mother Goddess, is borne between the wide pinions of the sky.

A totally different concept, sprung from the other side of the human imagination, saw the sun as being swallowed by Nut as it sank in the west, to pass through her and be reborn from her thighs with the sunrise. Yet even this idea could be combined with those of the boat and the beetle and also with the overriding idea of the eternal circuit of the sun—that having crossed the heavens by day it sailed round the netherworld or anti-heaven during the hours of darkness.

The sun was pushed by a beetle, sailed in a boat, flew upon wings, passed through the body of Nut—many were the variations of the imagery suggesting the transport of the sun. Yet when after the Hyksos invasion the war chariot was adopted in Egypt and the Pharaohs of the New Kingdom were everywhere shown beating down their enemies from the height of the royal car, this new and grandiose vehicle was never transferred to the sun. It is a sign of the intense religious conservatism of the Egyptians that it was so; although there were changes of emphasis at different periods, even quite profound changes of meaning and value, the old symbols and myths, the old divinities, were retained throughout the millennia.

The Sun God crossed the Nile valley from bright sunrise to reddened sunset and left the land to darkness and death. But the Egyptians also had him incarnate in their midst. Like all human beings since self-consciousness came to trouble them in the Stone Age, the Egyptians wanted to secure and harmonize their relationship with nature and the cosmos. They found this security and harmony through the being of their divine ruler. The living Pharaoh was identified with Horus, the Lord of Heaven. This had been true from very early times. On the huge slate palette of Narmer, probably the King Menes who according to tradition first united the Kingdom of Upper Egypt with that of the Delta, the sovereign is shown together with the falcon, both carved with all the clear confidence of the artists of a budding civilization. The relationship is often beautifully expressed, too, in later sculpture where the bird is shown sheltering the king's head between its wings. As sun gods both alike had golden flesh. Among the king's divine titles 'Horus of Gold' was often one, written by putting the falcon above the sign for gold. A Pharaoh of the Third Dynasty put the whole of his titles above this hieroglyph.

Pharaoh was Horus. Of all his divine forms this was the most ancient and unchanging. Yet the theological complexity was very great. For while the king was Harakhte, that flashing lord

93

of the sky, he was also the Horus who was the devoted son of Osiris, lord of the underworld. So every Pharaoh who in life had been Horus, in death became Osiris, his son rising from him again as Horus in endless cycle.

Although the idea of a solar cult of court and state in conflict with a popular mystery cult of Osiris has often been exaggerated, these two most powerful elements in Egyptian religion certainly were distinct in origin, and did represent two opposite approaches to the universe which had to be harmonized. The Sun God was at home in a celestial religion of triumph—he was Lord of Command and Intelligence, *Sol Invictus*—Osiris was a dying god of the earth and its fertility, at home in the chthonic mysteries of death and resurrection. They stood at the two poles of religious experience. Yet the drawing together of Shamash and Tammuz in Babylonia has already shown how the annual decline and return, and the daily rising and setting, of the sun could be equated with the death and resurrection of the vegetation and so serve to bring these opposites together. The Pharaoh who was at once the Sun God and Horus, and who at death became Osiris, was himself a powerful link between the two.

Yet Pharaoh was not the Sun God only as Horus. He was also identified in a rather different way with Re-Atum, the supreme creator. This identification was not as ancient as that with Horus, but it was to wax rapidly in importance during the Old Kingdom. Just north of Memphis or White Walls, the capital said to have been founded by Menes when he united the Two Kingdoms, was the great sun sanctuary of On or Heliopolis, the home of Atum-Re. The most sacred object in the temple, probably taking the place of a yet more ancient phallic column, was a tapering conical stone known as the *benben* which symbolized the Primeval Hill. The *benben* stone had solidified from the semen of Atum-Re as he created himself in the first sunrise. This myth was expressed in the later legend, followed by the Greek and Roman writers, which told how the

94

Sun God had first shown himself at Heliopolis, lighting on the *benben* in the form of a phoenix, golden-plumed bird of the sun.

The priesthood of the sanctuaries of Heliopolis grew powerful. Their theology in which Atum Re was the world creator began to triumph over that of other priesthoods, each of which gave its local god pre-eminence. It dominated even that of Memphis whose subtle teaching, centred upon their god Ptah, came very near to the Johannine doctrine—in the beginning was the Word. It seems probable that Atum, associated with the more primitive cult, receded into the background, and that the pure solar concept of Re filled the stage. So enduring was the triumph of Heliopolis to be that even in the Middle and New Kingdom when the capital of the Pharaohs had shifted far up the Nile to Thebes, the god of that city, Amon, had to be identified with Re and the reign of the Sun God continued.

The Pharaoh Djoser of the Third Dynasty had at his court a man of such brilliant parts that he can be called the first individual of genius to emerge into history with a name. No wonder that thousands of years later Imhotep was deified by the Greeks. The idea of the Pharaohs' tombs symbolizing the Primeval Hill had already begun, but Imhotep raised it to a higher level when he designed for Djoser the great Step Pyramid at Saqquara, a few miles outside Memphis. The flight of steps, either single or double, was the hieroglyphic sign for the Hill, and Djoser's pyramid gave it three-dimensional form. In the Fourth Dynasty it was developed into the true, straight-sided pyramid. Cheops, Chephren and Mycerinus built at Giza the tombs that were to become and remain the greatest of the Wonders of the World. The Great Pyramid of Cheops still surpasses in bulk any other building raised by man, and its height of 481 feet is out-topped among buildings made wholly of stone only by the slender spires of Cologne cathedral.

So in the service of the Sun God both on earth and in heaven, hosts of Egyptian workmen toiled daylong on the plateau of Giza, hammering, splitting and sawing—hauling

95

huge blocks to pile them up in casing after casing round the central core. Meanwhile away in the Muquattam hills other groups working under names such as the Vigorous Gang, the Sceptre Gang, the Enduring Gang, were cutting the finest lime-stone for the four outer facets of the pyramid so that they might reflect an answering gleam from the beams of Re. And far, far to the south other men again were hewing into the granite spur of the First Cataract, the rock made ruddy and crystalline by the inner fires of Earth, before floating great chunks of it down-stream to build the pyramid temples.

They toiled and sweated and some of them died. We remember them for what they did. They served the Sun God believing that the Sun God would serve them. Whether it was deluded or inspired, the human imagination, at a time still so near the dawn of civilization, was enabled to speak with a grandeur of expression that has never been silenced.

The Pharaohs of the Fourth Dynasty lived their ritual lives in supreme confidence of their godhead. They ruled as equals among the other high gods of the pantheon. With the follow-ing dynasty, however, the Heliopolitan priests seem to have ranged themselves round the king, exalting him as the divine head of their cult of Re, and so establishing it as an official state religion. The king was no less divine but he was less free—he had been made, as it were, a constitutional divinity. An inkling of these changes may have been embodied in the folk tale which recounts how the first three Pharaohs of this Dynasty were triplets begotten by Re on the wife of one of his priests at Heliopolis.

The tremendous power of the cult of Re in these later Old Kingdom times shows itself most clearly in the raising of mag-nificent sun temples. No fewer than six of the Fifth Dynasty Pharaohs built such temples, usually in addition to funerary pyramids. The one designed for Niuserrē just across the river from Heliopolis is the best known to us; probably the others closely resembled it. It was a temple built to rise up and up to its symbolic climax. The site chosen was itself a natural mound, and this was crowned with a wide platform mounted by steps. In a court on this stood a massive square plinth which in turn supported a heavy obelisk. The pyramidal apex of this obelisk, lifted high towards the sun, was perhaps sheathed in gold. Before the plinth was an alabaster altar with runnels cut in the surrounding pavement to carry the blood of sacrificial animals into nine basins of alabaster. Here in the open court where the pale stone dazzled with its brightness, Re was worshipped below the full might of his rays. But before reaching the open the officiating priests had passed through a long covered passage where exquisitely carved reliefs celebrated the seasons of the solar year, each with its appropriate plant and animal life and human activities. Here in the shadow Re was being praised alike as the lord of time and the cosmic cycle and as the creator of life in all its variety and delightful detail. Eight light minutes away in the heart of the star hydrogen was turned into helium and the radiations steeped our small planet just as they had for thousands of millions of years. But the consciousness which they had helped to bring into being could now respond with a new subtlety and grandeur.

The squat obelisk at the centre of worship in this and all the other Old Kingdom sun temples reveals more plainly than the slenderer form of later days that the pyramid forming the tip was the most important element, the shaft originally being hardly more than its support. The fact that the Egyptians saw their obelisks as symbolizing the sun's rays need not have prevented them from simultaneously seeing the pyramid as a symbol of the Primeval Hill. Nor need it have disturbed the belief that the *benben* stone at Heliopolis (probably the prototype of the obelisk) had solidified from the seed of Atum. In the turning kaleidoscope of man's religious imagination all fell into a pattern of cosmic beginnings—of the self-creating god, the first land, the first light.

Certainly the obelisk grew into the most graceful solar

symbol ever devised in the long history of sun worship. One specimen, which would have been the largest of them all, remains half-created in the granite quarries of Aswan, its sloping trunk still thick and rough-hewn, offering a pathway to tourists. As they pass along it, their dragomen throw pebbles to demonstrate the depth of the narrow shaft sunk beside it to enable the masons to wriggle down and work like moles upon the lower face. Today the finest obelisk is Queen Hatshepsut's at Karnak. Because when her memory was disgraced it was covered over, the sides now display the brilliant polish which was given to the pink granite, and the strong yet elegant incisiveness of the hieroglyphs. From the Greeks onwards, foreign visitors have marvelled at these monuments and coveted them, which is why many now stand in places of honour far from the rays of the Egyptian sun—beside the Thames, the Tiber and the Hudson, and one towering above the lamps in the Place de la Concorde.

The rising power of the state cult of Re during the Old Kingdom manifests itself not only in architectural forms, but also in abundant royal gifts of land to the god, and in the titles of Pharaoh himself. While in the Fourth Dynasty three Pharaohs, including the great pyramid builders Chephren and Mycerinus, compounded the god's name in their own, in the Fifth it became a usual element in all the royal cartouches, while the epithet of Son of Re also appeared regularly among the loyal titles.

In scores of texts inscribed in pyramid chambers, the royal dead were addressed as Sons of Re. They were to rejoin him at death to enjoy the afterlife in his company. From the Fifth Dynasty they might seek to serve him in some humble capacity. Thus among the fine hieroglyphs lining the walls of the funerary chambers of the Sixth Dynasty Pharaoh, Unas, are texts asking that the king should serve Re as his secretary, handling his muniment chests, opening his edicts, sealing his documents and sending out his messengers. And while every day the king would enjoy what was then the royal prerogative of accom-

98

panying the Sun God across the sky, he was not always too proud to help propel their barque. 'King Pepi receives to himself his oar; he takes his seat; he sits in the bow of the ship; he rows Re to the West.'

Although as time went by the Old Kingdom rulers were more and more closely associated with Re, until in the Sixth Dynasty they were occasionally quite identified with him— 'O Re thou art Teti and Teti is thou'—this was uncharacteristic. For while Pharaoh quite simply *was* Horus incarnate, his relationship with Re was different. He was his son, his successor, in a sense his repetition. In the beginning Re brought both life and order out of chaos, thus showing himself equally endowed with the two greatest powers of the Sun God throughout the world. As the supreme regulator he was father of the goddess Ma'at who personified a combination of perfect justice, truth and order. Because kingship was a part of the divine disposition from the moment of creation, Re was the first king of Egypt, and it remained the most profound purpose of each Pharaoh to maintain Ma'at, the order imposed by the creator. In this sense Re was the prototype of all the Pharaohs, and every reign was an image of his first reign.

The same word was used for sunrise, for the king's accession and for his first appearance on any occasion—on the throne, at the morning prayer—and was written with the hieroglyph that depicts the sun rising over the Primeval Hill. The throne echoed the same symbol, being set on the top of a small stepped pyramid.

So it was that all the images coincided, like similes illuminating the central poetic idea. They show the unity, the beautiful convergence of ideas underlying the confusion of Egyptian cosmology and religion. The self-creating Sun God rising on the first patch of dry ground among the waters of Nun; the newly fertilized soil still gleaming wet in the sun as the flood waters of the Nile began to recede, but soon, through the power of Osiris, to receive the lifeless seed and give it resurrection; the

99

return of the sun with the solar year; the daily victory of sunrise when Re defeated Apopophis, the serpent of darkness.
Then the reflection of these images in the being of Pharaoh.
His accession which was a greater sunrise, a re-enactment of the
first creation and the coming of light; his enthronement on
the summit of the Primeval Hill; the many ceremonies when
he confronted his celestial counterpart; his death into Osiris; the
placing of his body within the pyramid-hill whence he could
go to join Re in his barque and find eternal life in the unchanging cycles of the sun.

Before the end of the third millennium B.C. the Old Kingdom collapsed in dynastic feuds and civil strife. The impossible
had happened, Ma'at was overthrown. When we think of its
effect upon the Egyptians we have to remember that they had
no perspective, nothing to warn them that such a thing might
happen, for theirs was the first huge, rich and socially complex
kingdom in human history. There were no precedents.

Some sank into despair; it was recorded that the crocodiles
were sated with the flesh of suicides. The total breakdown of
authority was followed by social revolution. 'The bowman is
ready. The wrongdoer is everywhere. There is no man of
yesterday. A man goes out to plough taking his shield . . . The
robber is a possessor of riches.' And then 'He who possessed
no property is now a man of wealth. The poor man is full of
joy. Every town says: let us suppress the powerful among us.
The possessors of robes are now in rags. Jewels are fastened on
the necks of slave girls. Slave girls are free with their tongues.
When the mistress speaks it is irksome to the servants. The
children of princes are dashed against walls.'

Never again was the confidence of the Old Kingdom to be
fully restored. Just as we have lost the nineteenth-century faith
in the inevitability of progress, so the Egyptians lost their faith
in the inevitability of permanence. Although after a period of
feudalism a princely family of Thebes reunited the Two Kingdoms and founded the strong new line of Pharaohs of the

Twelfth Dynasty, it could never be forgotten that the Sun God incarnate had been overthrown, the throne of Re dishonoured. Literature remained pessimistic in tone, death was often praised as preferable to the uncertainties of life—and as a result the cult of Osiris began to have a stronger appeal. The god was now seen more clearly as king and judge of the dead, and whereas before only the Pharaoh could hope to become Osiris, now all men could follow him should their souls prove worthy of it. So already, though it did not go nearly so far as in the New Kingdom, there was a decline in the pride and delight in man, nature and this world which is so vivid in the art of the Old Kingdom, and an increasing interest in the next world and the strange spirits and creatures with which human imagination had peopled it. The upper world of sunlight gave ground to the underworld of darkness, the clarity of the conscious to the fantasy of the unconscious mind.

Yet it would be a grave mistake to suggest that the power of Re was seriously dimmed. Already in the Middle Kingdom he was being identified with Amon of Thebes, and Amon-Re King of the Gods was still supreme. Even in the underworld Osiris was not the final judge of souls, the dead had to present their case before a tribunal of gods with Re presiding over them. Moreover after so much suffering and despair, so much questioning of established hierarchies, the Egyptians passionately wanted to see Ma'at restored, but they recognized a new kind of justice. The idea of general kindliness, of social justice, of all men being equal in the sight of the gods, shines out from many Middle Kingdom texts. And as the creator and orderer it was Re who inspired and imposed the new morality. The sacrificial blood that flowed from the alabaster altar into the alabaster basins in his temples was no longer the food he most desired. 'More acceptable is the character of a man of just heart than the ox of the evildoer.'

It was at about this same time, some four thousand years ago, that the peoples of Mesopotamia were also passing from the idea of justice by favour to that of justice by right and were beginning to accept (however imperfectly they built upon it) a moral foundation for life. And there, too, as we have seen, it was the Sun God who sat in judgment. Yet perhaps because the Sumerians and Akkadians were tied to their pessimistic belief that men had been created only as slaves to the gods, the morality of Middle Kingdom Egypt at its highest seems a little more tender, the idea of love and equality a little more life-enhancing and warm.

What an extraordinary thing it was! Here was the spherical lump of matter which had come from the sun and was supported by it. In two small grooves worn upon it by moving water lived the little creatures who had emerged so very slowly from instinctive animal life, the energy for this whole evolutionary procession having been provided by the sun. Now at last, as they lived together and loved or hated one another and tried with their brave if puny minds to understand how their situation had come about, these beings, their simian origins still visible in every bone, brought into full flower ideas of goodness and right, of the strong giving way to the weak, the rich helping the poor. And the sun, which had in physical and historical fact done so much to build and order their lives, they made the creator and arbiter of the moral law.

The loftiest of the thoughts which the Middle Kingdom Egyptians found in their hearts and put into the mouth of Re as Creator, give full expression to the ideal of all men being of equal value and worthy of equal opportunity. It was only the iniquity of mankind itself that caused it to fall into tyranny and abuse. The Sun God says:

> I relate to you the four good deeds which my own heart did for me so that I might silence evil. I did four good deeds within the portal of the horizon.
>
> I made the four winds that every man might breathe thereof equally with his fellow. That is the first of the deeds.
>
> I made the great floodwaters that the poor man might have

rights in them like the great man. That is the second of the deeds.

I made every man like his fellow. I did not command that they might do evil; it was their hearts that violated what I had said. That is the third of the deeds.

I made that their hearts should cease from forgetting the west, in order that divine offerings might be made to the gods of the provinces. That is the fourth of the deeds.

Even the fourth deed, which smacks of propaganda, reveals the new care for the ordinary man and woman. For Re is saying that if they will remember eternal life and serve their local gods with piety all can attain 'the west', the land of sunset and the dead, and enjoy the eternity which once was the royal prerogative.

Many texts show the Sun God insisting upon justice for the people. In the address delivered by each Pharaoh to his Vizier, this highest official in the land is charged to be ever just, to show no preference to the rich, the powerful or the noble, but rather to favour the poor and timid. The king declares: 'Men expect justice from the Vizier's office, for justice has been its customary way since the reign of the Sun God upon earth.' Then the magnificent Tale of the Eloquent Peasant, a parable illustrating the ideal of justice for the humble, shows the spirit of Re presiding as the ultimate authority over all human law. The Peasant, whose asses have been seized by a rapacious petty official, turns to the Grand Steward for redress. Having made blistering attacks on official corruption and appealed to the Steward's known fairness, his final and successful plea is to divine authority. 'Do justice for the sake of the Lord of Justice [Re], thou . . . who are far from doing evil . . . Yet thou has not given me requital for this good word which came out of the mouth of Re himself: "speak the truth [Ma'at,] do the truth. For it is great, it is mighty, it is enduring."'

More than once the Eloquent Peasant uses the analogy of the scales to represent justice, asking in his indignation, 'Do the balances indeed swerve? Do the scales indeed incline to one side?" So the image which has had so universal an appreciation, which displays itself in the gilded and well-developed lady who holds her scales above the Law Courts in the heart of the City of London, was already present in the minds of the Egyptians four thousand years ago. And the god who, ultimately, held the scales was Re. This being so the Egyptians did not conceive the notion of a blindfolded impartiality to secure a fair balance. On the contrary, they, like so many other peoples, put their trust in the Sun God with his all-seeing eye to witness the truth and judge accordingly.

The Middle Kingdom, the age which saw the moral face of the Sun God at its brightest, ended in disaster even worse than that which had shattered the Old. The sanctity of the Nile valley was violated by Asiatic invaders, and their chiefs usurped the throne of the god. When at last after nearly two centuries the Hyksos were expelled and the traditional order re-established, the Egyptians, like the Russians in 1945, seized neighbouring territory to secure their frontier. Almost inevitably the success of this policy lured them on to further conquest in south-west Asia, and the people which had lived secure within the Nile valley found itself involved with all the riches and anxieties of Empire.

In the New Kingdom the second experience of failure and adversity led to a further strengthening of the cult of Osiris. Men turned more and more towards this god who was immanent in all humanity, who shared its suffering and death and offered the best hope of resurrection. So at this time Osiris took possession of the scales for the moral and ritual judging of the dead, and sometimes even usurped Re's judgment seat in the land of the living. As a result, interest in the idea of the Night Sun increased. The Sun God, it was held, sailed down into Osiris's kingdom in the underworld and there brought light and rejoicing to his subjects. Sometimes he shared the throne of Osiris, rather as Shamash had sat with Tammuz in the shade of the underworld tree.

It is probable, too, that the people were now more inclined to worship their Pharaoh as Horus the son of Osiris with his promise of resurrection than as Harakhte incarnate or as the son and image of Re. In the royal tombs of the valley of the Kings, although the figure of the Sun God and solar litanies appear at the entrance, Pharaoh's mummy was laid to rest among all manner of underworld scenes with all the weird creatures of the unconscious—serpents with feet and many heads, winged monsters and other beings of darkness that had to be slain or tamed.

Nevertheless, no more than in the Middle Kingdom was the reign of the Sun God seriously threatened, or the honour and worship offered him less. In the texts expressing the official theology his pre-eminence was always made clear, and the mythologies equally distinguish sharply between Osiris and the Great Gods and especially Re. One ventilates the idea in the form of an amusing folk-tale. In the absence of Re, Osiris assumed his throne and put on his crown 'that the gods might fear him'. But soon 'Osiris became ill in the head from the heat of the diadem of Re', and when the Sun God returned he found him with his head so much swollen that he had to draw off the blood and pus to save the presumptuous king of the underworld.

As for the honour paid to the Sun God, at what was now the immensely wealthy imperial capital of Thebes, the temples built for him far surpass in size and magnificence, if not in beauty, those of earlier days. Indeed the building now known as the Temple of Karnak, with its huge pylons, its obelisks and the famous peristyle hall of truly gigantic columns, together with the temple of Luxor, joined to it by an avenue of sphinxes and serving as its chapel of the New Year, make one of the half-dozen most prodigious architectural feats ever achieved by man.

The divinity worshipped at Karnak and Luxor was in fact Amon-Re. It has been shown how this identification of the gods of Heliopolis and of Thebes had taken place already in the

Middle Kingdom when the capital was first shifted from Memphis. It does not appear to have been merely the result of one of those mergers or take-over bids by which deities were amalgamated to please competing interests or affections. At Hermopolis Amon had been one of the eight gods of original chaos, representing the dynamic element of the wind. As men's thoughts grew more subtle, this wind god was seen to be the pneuma, the breath of life, the spirit. And as the priesthood of Amon rose to power with their city, they did not question the ancient supremacy of Re, but in uniting him with their own god recognized the beauty and completeness of a deity compounded of the creator sun and the breath of life, of light and spirit.

As for the continuing strength of the relationship between king and Amon-Re, it is apparent in all manner of New Kingdom records. One is distinctive. That remarkable woman, Queen Hatshepsut of the Eighteenth Dynasty, having to justify her rule as Pharaoh, depicted in her lovely temple of Der el-Bahri her begetting by the god who had assumed the body of her father Tuthmosis I. The inscriptions explain the impregnation of the Queen Mother: 'Amon-Re took his form as the majesty of this her husband, the king Tuthmosis . . . Then he went to her immediately and had intercourse with her . . . Amon, Lord of the Two Lands, spoke in her presence. Now . . . Hatshepsut is the name of this my daughter whom I have placed in thy body. She is to exercise beneficent kingship in the entire land.'

A generation or so later the relationship of king and sun is finely expressed in the account of Amenhotep II's accession, which appropriately took place at dawn.

> *King Tuthmosis III went up to heaven;*
> *He was united with the sun disk;*
> *The body of the god joined him who had made him*
> *When the next morning dawned*
> *The sun disk shone forth,*

The sky became bright,
King Amenhotep II was installed on the throne of his father.

I have shown how the Sun God, Re, was at once the creator of life, and the judge and orderer. How his aspect as moral arbiter attained a full and sometimes noble development in the Middle Kingdom, and how after uniting with Amon he came to be understood as a god of light and spirit by the more sensitive religious minds of the New Kingdom. Yet for what to me is the most significant, because the most characteristic, face of the Sun God in Egypt I look back to the Old Kingdom and the joyful celebration of Re as the creator of the abundant life of this world. To the passage-way of the sun temple of Niuserrē with its flowers and animals and the changing agricultural life of the seasons of Inundation, Winter and Spring. For it was this jubilant, life-creating Sun God who was revived and lifted to unequalled heights during that unique episode in Egyptian history, the religious revolution of Akhenaten.

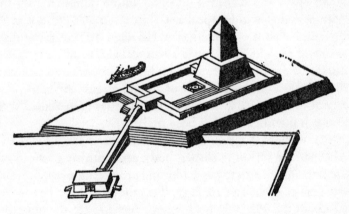

SUN TEMPLE OF NIUSERRĒ NEAR HELIOPOLIS

SUN OF LIFE

ALMOST EVERY ESTIMATE has by now been made of the character and achievements of Akhenaten, this extraordinary young Pharaoh of the Eighteenth Dynasty. He has been hailed as the first individual in history, as a religious genius who was the first man on earth to have the vision of a single god of all lands and peoples—and he has been knocked down again as a half-mad epileptic whose obsession with the Aten was due to a fanatical self-absorption and did not at all deserve the name of monotheism. His reign has been recognized as one of the glories of Egypt's past and also as an unmitigated disaster when the empire won by his predecessors was allowed to crumble away by the folly of a blind idealist. Even the new school of art which flowered at his court has been abused with as much intensity as it has been praised.

The truth is, I think, that the tremendous force lodged in Akhenaten's curiously shaped body acts with magnetic force upon us all, we turn towards him and project our prejudices and our desires. I make no apology, then, for refusing to be moderate about this Pharaoh, for I believe detachment, the objective view, to be impossible. He had what I most admire, a brilliant and potent imagination, an artist's power, making his reign one of those beacons along the roads of history which without them would be so dark and dreary. And in a study of man and the sun, his importance cannot be challenged.

In my eyes those who have reacted so brutally against the simple enthusiasm of Breasted and other early admirers of Akhenaten, exhibit all the attitudes of the conservative conformist, the man (especially common in the Anglo-Saxon world) who, if he cannot fairly be called Philistine, is certainly anti-aesthetic. The type, in short, who distrusts thought, feeling and imagination, preferring to put his trust in discipline, convention and cold baths.

Such characters condemn the Pharaoh (known to have been far from robust) for 'lolling effeminately upon a cushioned chair', or for being portrayed on terms of intimate affection with his wife and little daughters, when they say nothing against all those countless scenes showing other 'manly' Pharaohs engaged in slaughtering wild life, trampling enemies, holding prisoners by the hair in preparation for dispatching them, proudly contemplating piles of severed hands. They condemn him for neglecting the military ideals of Empire, for upsetting the traditional Establishment of the priesthood of Amon; they condemn the 'immaturity' of his vision of a universal god immanent in the life and joy of nature and of men and women. They condemn his new art as 'hideous', just as they condemn the new art of their own day.

Yet, as always, the creations of the original genius they try to belittle give them the lie. They cannot suppress the fact that Akhenaten's Sun Hymn and other religious literature of his inspiration have a beauty of expression and an understanding of spiritual values far in advance of their time. They cannot conceal from anyone with ready eyes the new life in the art of el Amarna, or deny the sheer wonder of a young man who could defeat the vested interests of court and capital and in a few years give reality to a dream city, a city founded upon the enjoyment of nature, of art and of mortal and immortal love.

It is my belief that if only south-west Asia and the Mediterranean had been ready for it, if only there had been a St. Paul of the Sun, and the religion of the divine Akhenaten and his father the Aten had reached the hearts and minds of the civilized peoples of the day, then there need have been none of the glorification of militaristic empires so characteristic of the ensuing age. The recognition of ideals more worthy of humanity, of the ideals we have now to embrace if we are not to perish, might have appeared as the inevitable course of history. But it could not be. The light of the Aten hardly shed its full radiance beyond those fourteen boundary stones of the Pharaoh's city at el Amarna. Christianity had to adapt itself to a world which had been shaped and hardened by the ideas of glory shared by the Egyptians of Ramses, the Assyrians, the Medes and Persians, the imperial Romans.

Akhenaten passed his childhood in surroundings both rich and worldly. His father, Amenophis III, had a long and successful reign, and tribute and gifts of all kinds flowed into Thebes from Nubia in the south to Babylonia and the lands of the Mitanni in the north. Amenophis seems to have kept a keen appetite for women, and in his middle age young princesses from both the Mitannian and Babylonian royal families came with trains of ladies-in-waiting and attendants to join his household. Yet Akhenaten's mother Tiye, a woman of powerful personality, saw to it that their realm did not extend far enough beyond the bed to threaten her position as Great Wife of the king.

From a tender age Akhenaten is likely to have responded to the charm of his parents' new palace on the west side of the Nile, to the paintings of birds and animals and flowers that covered the walls, to its gardens and the artificial lake made nearby for his mother's pleasure.

I would venture to guess that while he never questioned the luxury and splendour of the royal state, or the ostentatious wealth of Thebes, as he grew older he may already have begun to dislike the priestly politicians of the temples of Amon. He may have found the whole life of the Establishment dreadfully ponderous—to his visionary mind as heavy and unspiritual as the huge seated statues of his father which had been erected before the façade of Amenophis's great mortuary temple a mile or two from the palace. That they were to survive and gain a kind of enchantment as the Colossi of Memnon even his poetic imagination could not have foreseen.

I think, too, that this boy would not have responded eagerly to the stories and pictures of the warlike prowess of his ancestors or have wished to school himself in exercises with the bow and spear. More likely, restricted by his epilepsy, he would have spent much time with the women of the court, all of whom, and not least the many foreign ladies, would have wished to spoil him, to tell him tales. So his mind would have been accustomed to imagine countries and customs and beliefs far removed from those of Egypt. If he ever heard accounts of the art- and nature-loving life of the former Knossos (and presents reached his father from Crete) it may well have fascinated him and seemed far more sympathetic than the stiff ritual of his home.

The priesthood of Amon, with its temples on both sides of the Nile being extended and increased with every reign, and endowment added to endowment, was immensely rich and influential. Nearly a century before, Tuthmosis III had united all the priesthoods of Egypt, including the proud and ancient hierarchy of Heliopolis, into one national body, and put the High Priest of Amon at its head. More than once since then this primate had combined the office with that of Grand Vizier, so assuming a position of unrivalled power. At Heliopolis the High Priest still kept his ancient title of Great Seer, and it is probable that he and his priesthood, which had an ancient tradition of astronomical knowledge, remained more spiritual and intellectual, less openly political, than the Theban college. Whether or no Heliopolis had anything to do with it, there are signs that already during the reign of Amenophis III, although that Pharaoh heaped wealth upon Amon, there was a court party interested in strengthening the purely solar aspect of

Amon-Re, and in general favouring the ancient royal tradition of the Sun God at the expense of Theban Amon and his overweening priests.

Two architects, twin brothers, employed by Amenophis III in his great buildings in Thebes, inscribed a stela there with an eloquent sun hymn. It was entitled 'Adoration of Amon when he rises as Harakhte', an indication that it was addressed to the Theban divinity solely as Sun God. It shows how already the wider horizons of imperial life were causing all thinking men to see religion in more universal terms.

> *Sole Lord taking captive all lands every day,*
> *As one beholding them that walk therein;*
> . . .
> *He makes the seasons by months,*
> *Heat when he desires,*
> *Cold when he desires.*
> *He makes the limbs to languish when he enfolds them,*
> *Every land is in rejoicing*
> *At his rising every day, in order to praise him.*

This poem, the earliest to convey unambiguously the idea of the Sun God pouring his divinity upon all lands and peoples, includes several mentions of the sun disk or Aten. There is, indeed, an increase in the use of this title for the sun in the texts of the reign of Amenophis. More significant, the inscriptions in the tomb of a Theban noble record that he was Steward in the Mansion of the Aten. Again, one of the royal barges in which Queen Tiye could glide on her pleasure lake was given the bewitching name of *Aten Gleams*. Even if the boat was not quite so delicious as the one Shakespeare furnished for Cleopatra, and if it could not possibly be said of Tiye that 'For her own person, it beggar'd all description . . . o'er picturing . . . Venus', the young prince probably had happy memories of sailing with his mother in the *Aten Gleams*.

It has been suggested that this form of the Sun God was

exalted to avoid the contention between the priests of Amon
and the court party looking back to the ancient cult of Re. If
so, then the result was ironical indeed. Whatever Akhenaten's
good or bad qualities, he was no lover of compromise.

When the prince succeeded on the death of his father in
about 1367 B.C. he was still hardly more than a boy—although
his age is uncertain. One can imagine that for one of his
temperament the mysteries and solemn rituals which took place
amid the majestic architecture of the capital when, at sunrise,
he mounted to the throne of Re, would have had an overwhelming emotional effect. Now he had acceded to godhead.
Among all the profound changes of his reign, there is no sign
that he ever questioned this one essential belief.

At first he was content to keep the name of Amenophis IV
and Thebes as his capital. In his tentative steps towards religious
change he was still looking towards Heliopolis. He determined
to add more buildings to the already bewildering maze of
temples at Karnak. In the quarry where stone was hewn for the
purpose the young Pharaoh is shown worshipping Amon-Re,
but with an inscription in which he describes himself as 'First
prophet of Re-Harakhte Rejoicing-in-the-Horizon in his name
the sunlight which is Aten'. This elaborate title shows the future
Akhenaten poised between the old ideas of Heliopolis and new
ones forming in his imagination. Indeed, even while he remained at Thebes, he caused one profound change to be made
in the symbolism of the Sun God which shows how far he had
already gone towards the worship of the Aten. Over a large
area inside the precinct wall of Karnak, principally in the
neighbourhood of the gloomy temple of the Moon God, there
are long, meaningless walls of fragmented stone. On the outer
face each fragment has a smoothed and whitened surface bearing some scrap of carving in low relief, the pigments often still
clinging to it. These walls have been stacked by the explorers of
recent times and the shattered stones represent what was left of
Akhenaten's temples when his faith had been overthrown and

the traditionalists had let loose all their hate on the monuments of a religion of love. As I walked slowly along one of these walls thinking about the passionate hatred which is always engendered when the worse reacts against the better, I began to notice how many of the carved surfaces displayed simply a slender bar painted a golden yellow. Then I came upon one in which the bar did not cross the face but terminated in a stiff little curved hand. Then with a dawning delight I saw how all the yellow bars were segments from the rays of the Aten, each one of which would have started from the sun's disk and ended with a hand casting divine force upon all life below. Already, then, in his buildings at Thebes the Pharaoh had devised this inspired symbol of his life-giving god which was to be so freely used when he came to decorate his own fair city of the Aten.

Round the peristyle court of the chief of his temples here at Karnak were set up colossal statues of the Pharaoh carved in the new mood. They have been almost universally condemned as grotesque and hideous. To me they are not so at all. The long face is mobile and sensitive yet strong, and the whole body has a nerve, a restrained movement and life—a kind of eagerness. It is true that the full, curving hips are not the ideal of manly physique, but, aesthetically, full hips are no less pleasing than square shoulders—rather the reverse. There seems no doubt that the youth did in truth possess this somewhat feminine figure. If he ordered his sculptors to emphasize it, then perhaps unconsciously he was giving expression to something profound in his imagination. To my mind the religion and way of life he was to initiate gave full expression to the feminine principle.

There is another more famous instance of the beginning of the religious and artistic revolution at Thebes. Among the tombs of the nobles on the western bank of the Nile is one belonging to the Vizier Ra'mose. As you enter and grow accustomed to the faint light of the anteroom, you see all the left-hand part of the room decorated with reliefs, excellent of their kind but of the familiar formal style of Egyptian tradition.

An inscription dates them to the reign of Amenophis IV, and the king is shown in the conventional manner. But in the reliefs on the right-hand side of the dark doorway leading into the tomb chamber, treatment and feeling are completely different. The Pharaoh with his queen, Nefertiti, are leaning eagerly from a balcony giving golden necklets to the vizier. Servants and attendants bowing with smiles upon their lips surround them, while from above the Aten with its great fan of rays presides over all. Further to the right again, a scene of men belonging to different races has been sketched on the stone in the same lively style, but was never carved. Perhaps Ra'mose died, or perhaps work was stopped by the removal of the court from Thebes.

The contrast between the scenes on either hand of that Theban tomb entry sums up not only the artistic revolution and the worship of the Aten, but much of the wider revolution as well. On the left (perhaps it would have been more appropriate to accepted political terminology to have named the walls from the point of view of the intended corpse) is the enduring Egyptian Establishment, every face, every limb, expressing the conviction that nothing must change, nothing must move—they are impassive, dignified, frigid. On the right every muscle is in action, every face and body charged with emotion; people move and feel in relation to one another. On the left are timelessness and the impersonal, on the right quick movement and vivid individuality.

In the sixth year of the reign the crisis came. Amenophis IV changed his name to Akhenaten (Aten is Satisfied), and left the splendours of the richest capital on earth to build his own ideal city which he was to call Akhetaten, the Horizon of the Aten. What finally caused the break we cannot tell. No doubt that while they had to pay lip service to the divinity of Pharaoh, the priests of Amon, and the civil rulers who were one with them, opposed him at every turn, impeding all his plans with the weight of their traditions and their determination to hold fast to power. Probably, too, as his inner vision of a single godhead free from tangible form, the source of all energy and life, grew stronger and brighter and more irresistible, he found Thebes with its host of bizarre gods, its ugly popular rites and superstitions, an intolerable presence. So he left to start anew on uncontaminated soil where his ideals could flower in their own air.

It can be said that in this Akhenaten showed the escapism of the blind idealist, the folly of hoping that the past can be left behind. Yet to him it would have appeared the only way of bringing to pass all that he thought greatest and best. And he went without causing civil war, without anger or executions; he remained on loving terms with his mother who stayed behind, and he continued to honour the memory of his father. He could believe, too, that he was only purifying and exalting the ancient religion of Heliopolis against the upstart cult of Amon. He never ceased to call himself Son of Re and so to maintain the image of the inherited throne.

He himself led the expedition to choose the site of the new city of the Sun God. Probably he travelled in his royal barge, experiencing himself as the Sun God in his barque. About halfway between Thebes and the sea he saw what he must instantly have felt to be the ideal place for the fulfilment of his dream. The cliffs of the eastern desert swung away from the river, formed a great arc reaching as much as three miles from the Nile before returning to it seven miles further north. On the crescent of land so enclosed there was plenty of space for a great city, it was free—'Behold the Pharaoh found that it belonged not to a god nor to a goddess, it belonged not to a prince, nor to a princess', and, which probably appealed most of all to his emotional needs, it was isolated—a little private kingdom protected by the wall of cliffs. At first he intended to limit his domain to the east bank, but later he carried it as far as the cliffs on the opposite side, probably to embrace enough fields to make his community more nearly self-supporting.

The young king identified himself passionately with his chosen land. It was his and his divine father's. When he returned to the site for the foundation ceremonies 'mounting in a great chariot of electrum' he drove to the first boundary stone of Akhetaten and, as is recorded on the stela itself, told his subjects 'Ye behold the city of the Horizon of Aten which the Aten has desired me to make for him as a monument in the great name of my majesty for ever. For it was the Aten, my Father, who brought me to this City of the Horizon. There was not a noble who directed me to it; there was not any man in the whole land who led me to it. . . . Nay, it was the Aten, my Father, who directed me to make it for him.' His subjects repeated that this was so, that peoples of all lands would bring tribute to the Aten, 'him that made their life, and by whose rays one lives and breathes the air. May he grant eternity in seeing his rays. Verily the City of the Horizon will thrive like Aten in heaven for ever and ever.' In the rest of this long inscription, moving because in spite of the formal language it reveals so clearly the workings of the young man's heart, he describes the temples and palaces he will build for the god, himself and Nefertiti, and how tombs shall be prepared for himself and his wife and daughter, to which he swears their bodies shall be returned even if they die in a distant place. Most urgently of all he insists that nothing, not even the persuasions of Nefertiti, will make him move his city from this spot chosen by his god 'which he did enclose for his own self with cliffs', nor will he extend in any direction beyond the limits marked by his stelae.

It has been thought that this insistence on keeping within appointed bounds might have been to satisfy his old enemies, but to me it seems evident that instead it was to satisfy his own psychological urges. He wanted Akhetaten to be like an island fastness, a piece of virgin land undefiled by the worship of baser gods where he could live with his family and followers cut off from the world, and where he could rejoice when his god rose daily in his temple 'and fills it with his beams, beauteous in love, and lays them upon me in life and length of days for ever'. He was determined to keep his little holy land apart. Indeed he was retreating to it as to a monastery, but a monastery where, instead of being denied, the senses given by God were to be exercised and refined.

In the eighth year of his reign Akhenaten was able to quit Thebes with his family and all those courtiers who genuinely or for convenience were converts to his faith. It was a royal removal on an unprecedented scale, as the Pharaoh, Nefertiti and their three daughters sailed for the Horizon of the Aten. How wonderful to move not into a new house but into a new city. It stood there waiting for them. There was the great temple of the god, over two hundred yards long, and other sacred buildings including one where the queen in all her loveliness was nightly to celebrate the setting of the divine disk even as her husband had celebrated its rising; there was a palace for the king and another for the queen set beside delicious gardens near the river; there were the houses of the nobles and the houses of the sculptors and other artists, bright with paintings of birds and flowers, and with gardens set with ponds and kiosks and statuary and all the light-hearted furniture appropriate to the new way of life.

This new way, so far as the royal household was concerned, was to be more free, spontaneous and natural. Akhenaten did not want the honour paid him as a divinity and the son of the sun to be lessened, but nor did he want to appear only as a distant figure performing ritual acts like a divine automaton. The enjoyment of life and love was an essential part of the worship of the true god, so he had himself and Nefertiti portrayed tenderly embracing and kissing one another, dandling their daughters, sitting at table and biting at a cutlet or a pigeon. Evidently in real life they wandered freely in their gardens, visited the artists' studios and drove, the whole family together, about the streets of Akhetaten.

IV. AKHENATEN AND NEFERTITI MAKE OFFERINGS TO THE ATEN

The art which the Pharaoh inspired has often been said to show a new naturalism. This is not true; the traditional art of Egypt is far more dedicated to a careful portrayal of appearances. The art which began at Thebes and flourished in the aesthetic atmosphere of Akhetaten was, on the contrary, one of exaggeration and curious mannerisms. What was new in it was the movement, the sense of the moment, the portrayal of emotion and of relationships. Art and life alike in Akhetaten were to express the king's fresh understanding of Ma'at—a vision of truth avoiding all stiffness and pretence. The king constantly refers to himself as 'Living in Truth' and his city as the 'Seat of Truth'. Men and nature were to stand naked before their god, rejoicing in the light and heat of his rays.

To gain an insight into the profundity of the religious revolution conceived by the genius and brought about by the will of Akhenaten it is only necessary to read his famous Sun Hymn printed at the end of this book. It shows a full spiritual realization of the idea of a universal god which had had its faint dawn in the previous reign; it is highly charged with the sense of the sole god's universal and all-pervading love.

> *When you shone from the eastern horizon*
> *You filled every land with your beauty.*
> *You are lovely, great and glittering,*
> *You go high above the lands you have made,*
> *Embracing them with your rays,*
> *Holding them fast for your beloved son.*

There is an ecstatic delight in the beneficent power of god manifest in nature, the power that makes the birds lift up their wings in adoration, makes the sheep skip and the fish leap, calls the chick from the egg, quickens the human child in the mother's womb. Throughout the whole hymn, there is no threat, no judgment, no fear of darkness. Moreover, although it is full of intense poetry it is also supremely rational. Here indeed is religion true to the light of the sun.

It is important to remember, too, the murk which this light dispelled. The whole preoccupation with the underworld and its horrific monsters, of buying charms and other magical devices for defeating or escaping them—the same silly devices for hoodwinking the deity which were to reappear in the purchase of pardons—were repugnant to Akhenaten and were almost entirely kept out of his city. With them went all the sacred animals, the pantheon of animal-headed or phallic gods (Min had been much in evidence in Thebes). Only Re remained, and he was as much the Aten as Jesus was the Christ.

On the social side of his revolution, Akhenaten rejected the assumption of the inferiority of foreigners and women. In his hymn he offers praise for the creation of the Syrians and Nubians before mentioning the Egyptians; instead of disparaging, he marvels at racial differences: 'Men speak in many tongues, in body and complexion they are various, for you have distinguished between people and people.' He marvels, too, at the providence of god in providing other lands with rain to take the place of the river which to him was the normal source of water: 'How excellent are your purposes, O lord of eternity! You have set a Nile in the sky for the strangers, for the cattle of every country that go upon their feet.'

With this inner realization of human brotherhood it was inescapable that the king should have felt deeply against war and refused to press his armies against Egypt's Asiatic rivals.

His attitude to women is expressed in the instruction he must have given to his artists to portray his beloved Nefertiti on terms of equality with himself. A domestic ideal of the husband and father intimate with his wife and children seems to have been set before the court. Nefertiti is shown as his close and constant companion. He spoke of her always as 'mistress of his happiness', as 'lady of grace', 'great love'. This attitude he expected his nobles and other followers to emulate. Then at Akhetaten it was no longer thought right to boast of a noble ancestry. True, with the ancient Establishment against him, the Pharaoh was encouraged to promote those of modest birth, yet it is impossible to separate his feeling for the humbly born from his feeling for foreigners and women. He saw them as all of equal worth as all alike were blessed by the rays of the sun.

That aspect of the Sun God elsewhere concerned with order, judgment and hence with fixed ethics had little place in the religion of the Aten. The vision of the king was creative and positive. If men lived in the light of human and divine love and accepted his concept of Ma'at as a wholly truthful way of life, there was no need for the scales, the rod, and an enforced morality.

It is truly marvellous that this young man living over three thousand years ago should have seen and acted upon nearly all those ideals towards which we are still struggling. Truly marvellous that he should have been able to create what he at least believed to be his ideal society in its perfect setting on that little crescent of land hemmed in by the vast deserts of North Africa. But what seems to me even more extraordinary is the extent to which his religious vision coincided with the facts of our existence as they have been revealed to us in recent times.

He chose the name of the Aten which had always in the past come nearest to a matter-of-fact name for the physical being of the sun. The divine power in it which he worshipped was first called quite simply heat, but later was changed to a word usually translated effulgence or radiance. Akhenaten was clear, too, that the star was distant and only sent its rays to the earth: 'Though you are far away, your rays are on earth; though you fill men's eyes, your footprints are unseen.' He spoke, too, of how 'the Aten shone on him in life and length of days, invigorating his body each day'. Always and always he spoke of the life-giving rays—the idea of universal bounty symbolized by the disk and the many hands.

It seems as though he knew by intuition of the mighty burning body in the heavens, of the principle of radiation and the fact that this radiation supplied all the energy for life on earth. He even saw how it was the power of the sun that made the Nile and caused its rising. Yet he looked beyond these things, speaking of the Master of the Aten, and equating the physical radiance of the sunshine with a universal creative love:

Thou art shining, beautiful and strong;
Thy love is great and mighty,
Thy rays are cast into every face,
Thy glowing hue brings life to hearts.

It is a vision very similar to that of Valencio and the Pueblo Indians of a Great Spirit behind the sun's disk, but more subtle, refined, exalted. It is a vision, too, of all of us who believe there to be some higher existence beyond our present human comprehension. Today we have factual evidence for the hydrogen and helium furnace at the heart of the sun and its release of nuclear energy; for the heat and light waves rushing down to earth; for the energy they provide, the carbon they manufacture in plants. We know that without this radiance, this effulgence, life could never have begun, consciousness could never have dawned. Yet we can also divine that these nuclear and atomic and chemical reactions are at the command of some greater force, some Master of the Aten, and that the consciousness perceiving this is itself an aspect of the higher level of being.

Of course Akhenaten failed. The dispossessed priesthood of Amon led the reaction; the people, never willingly parted from their magic and idolatory, readily followed; the neighbouring powers took advantage of the anti-militarist king. We do not even know how Akhenaten and Nefertiti ended their days, save that they were pushed aside, their faith overthrown. After three thousand years of history, after the failure of so many religions, the fall of so many civilizations, the strength and violence of the dark side of man, his underworld of evil, is known to us only too well and the failure appears inevitable.

But to the young man with no sad pages of history to turn it was otherwise. We cannot blame him if he could not see that the world was not ready for his ideals, and that the god who possessed him could not possess other men until their hearts and minds had grown towards him. We can only blame ourselves that even now we are not ready.

In the remaining centuries of the New Kingdom the Sun God in his more materialistic aspect of Amon-Re continued to be honoured. The temples at Thebes were made yet more grandiose, the images of this King of the Gods and the rest of his pantheon were carved and painted and modelled in their thousands. The names of the Aten and his royal prophet were erased, their sanctuaries pulled down and the fragments used for the temples of other gods. And as the might and prosperity of Egypt declined men turned more and more to Osiris, lord of the underworld. The Pharaohs were laid to rest in their tombs cut deep into the rock of the Theban hills in chambers whose walls were crawling with serpents and other black-painted creatures of darkness. Some even lay in their coffins surrounded by rows of decapitated prisoners proving the glory of empire with the stumps of their necks.

I will evoke only one monument of this age to end the story of the Sun God in Egypt: the Great Temple at Abu Simbel. Ramses II, who achieved a last flurry of imperial grandeur when decline was in fact already close at hand, carved this extraordinary building deep into the sandstone cliffs of Lower Nubia. On the façade are four enormous seated statues of himself, two on either side of a central door. This narrow entry, surmounted by a Horus with vigorous human body and sun-crested falcon head, leads into a dim chamber where two lines of towering figures of the Pharaoh as Osiris, holding the crook and flail, confront one another across the central aisle. The walls of the hall are embellished with fine but brutal scenes of the war against the Hittites. Still deeper, and much darker, is the inner shrine where the king sits side by side with the supreme gods Amon, Horus and Ptah. The temple faces east-ward across the Nile, and at sunrise the first rays briefly shine through the entry, penetrating the darkness to strike the four gloomy deities where they sit so far within the rock. At the same time, in a tiny adjacent temple now dismantled, the beams used to slant through a fissure to light an altar watched over by four sun-worshipping baboons.

Yes, Abu Simbel shows that the Sun God was still powerful and still honoured, but there was nothing in the temple that could have touched the spirit of Akhenaten. Nor was there anything of promise for the future.

EGYPTIAN SUNBOAT
From *The Book of the Dead*

SUN OF DEATH

IN EGYPT A solar cult of extraordinary power was centred on the royal house and the person of the Pharaoh. One of these kings, Akhenaten, born with a native genius that one might well recognize as a spark of divinity, lifted the religion of the sun to the greatest height it was ever to attain. Indeed, in my eyes the religious vision which found living expression at Akhetaten was as true and fine as any ever realized in the mind of man. It had much in common with the early centuries of Christianity—of the faith recorded in the buildings of Ravenna where the prevailing symbols are those of life—birds, flowers, trees—in place of the cross and the crown of thorns that were so soon to displace them. It was weak in that it ignored the dark side of life, and perhaps could not entirely satisfy the simple desires of ordinary, labouring, suffering men and women. Yet as a religion of love and life and gratitude for all that the earth has to offer below the sun, it has never been surpassed.

Between two and three thousand years later, and far away on the other side of the globe, other royal houses almost equally mighty were to emerge and identify themselves with the solar power. So striking was the analogue that it led W. J. Perry to imagine a world-wide archaic civilization originating in Egypt and carried by a ruling class of Children of the Sun across all oceans and continents. Ignoring the identity of experience stored in the conscious and unconscious mind of man, he thought that such similarities could only have been brought about by the movement of bodies.

I wish to recall the civilizations of Central and South America not so much because of the similarities between the ideas emerging in two hemispheres, as because in the end their manifestations were in utter contrast. While Akhenaten raised the Sun God to his noblest and most spiritual, the Aztecs were to degrade him with blood and war, to make him a prince not of light but of darkness.

Yet this is not the only reason for turning in this chapter to the New World. Even while the Aztecs within the lofty basin of the Valley of Mexico were feeding their dreadfully imagined divinity on palpitating human hearts, and displaying the skulls of the victims by the thousand in the centre of their capital, the Incas had enthroned a Sun God of yet another aspect in their extraordinary kingdom among the peaks of the Andes. There he was to be the centre of an iron paternalism, a benevolent tyranny, that makes the citizens of present-day Russia seem all but free. Here, then, is yet another form of the relationship of man and the sun which cannot be omitted from this chronicle.

Looking at world history through the widest-angled lens available, nothing in the whole vast spectacle is more compelling than the division of man between the two hemispheres, his separate and yet parallel development on two land masses so remote from one another that they shared only the common bond of the human mind. Owing to the pattern of evolution from the earliest times, the Americas tended to follow in the wake of the Old World. It was only late in the last Ice Age, when all the less able types of human being had been eliminated and *Homo sapiens* had long been in possession of Asia, Europe and Africa, that men began to push across the frozen wastes of land and sea of Siberia and Alaska and then fan out to people an enormous double continent where no human being had ever set foot before them.

The invaders entered America as hunters and food gatherers, and although probably further groups continued to trickle in over several thousands of years, even overlapping with the time when farming was being perfected far off in south-west Asia, there is no evidence that the civilizations of the Old World had any influence whatever on those which were to grow up in the New. Yet when at last these two worlds were to be abruptly confronted, the Spanish Conquistadors in both Mexico and Peru found themselves entering cities where the palaces, temples and gardens filled them with wonder and admiration.

When Egypt and Sumeria were flourishing, there was no high civilization in the Americas, although simple agriculture had probably already begun. Indeed, it was not until about the time of Christ that certain regions in Central America and the northern Andes and their adjacent coast began to forge ahead of the rest of the continent. Although such historical equations are dangerous, one can take the Pueblo Indians as representing this stage, and indeed of still sharing in a common inheritance with the civilization of the Maya, the Incas and the Aztecs. This appears not only in such large matters as their worship of the Sun God. I have already described how when I was in a Pueblo house watching a ceremonial dance of the masked gods, I found myself sitting on the floor beside a little wooden shrine showing the four quarters of the world and the pole of nadir and zenith. This was a concept of great influence among all three peoples; indeed the Incas called their kingdom Four Regions and the lines dividing them crossed at their capital at Cuzco, dividing the city itself into four quarters. Thus the flimsy little contraption set out on that hut floor in Zuni was a whispered echo of an idea once developed on an imperial scale. It is not unreasonable to suppose that the Sun God of Valencio and his fellow priests also contains some elements known to the founders of the high civilizations.

If the Aten was the God of Love, the Sun God of the Incas

127

may be said to have been God the Father. As with the Egyptians, the supreme ruler, the Sapa Inca or Unique Inca, was from the first identified with a royal solar cult. One of his titles was Intip Cori, meaning Son of the Sun, and in one of the legends concerning the founding of the kingdom it was his father the sun who sent the first Inca out with his sister-wife to establish a city wherever a golden wand he was given should sink into the ground. This happened at Cuzco, a site beautifully set at the head of a gently sloping valley over 11,000 feet above the sea. The tale certainly represents an historical occupation of the valley by a people who had come from some region not very far distant, probably in about A.D. 1200.

For some two centuries the Incas ruled a small kingdom from a modest capital, engaging in no more than local wars and skirmishes. Then, in the fifteenth century, two strong and ambitious rulers, Pachacuti and his son Topa Inca, achieved a series of conquests of neighbouring peoples, first among the tribes of the high Andes, but later boldly extending to the Chimu and other powerful dwellers along the coast. These were no temporary conquests such as had occurred sporadically in the past, but a steady process of empire building, showing a genius for administration which seems to have belonged to Pachacuti. Everywhere that they went the Incas extended their marvellous roads, their system of imperial messengers, their extraordinarily perfect structure of social control and the large bureaucracy that inevitably accompanied it. And as an integral part of this organization they also introduced the royal cult of the sun. Soon in towns and villages all over the provinces of the Empire sun temples were built where the divine Son of the Sun was worshipped as well as the Sun God himself. These can be likened to the temples to the deified emperor, such as that dedicated to Claudius at Colchester, which everywhere followed the conquering Roman legions. The most important of them was at Pachacamac, near Lima, where for centuries there had been a great temple to a supreme creator god of this name. So it was that by the time of the Spanish conquest a territory stretching from Equador to northern Chile had been forged into a vast sun kingdom presided over in absolute if benevolent might by the Intip Cori.

This apex of the tightly constructed pyramid of Inca society, this gold-encrusted solar king, was an hereditary monarch, the son, though not necessarily the eldest, of the previous Inca and his Chief Wife or Qoya. He normally (probably more regularly than the Egyptian Pharaoh) took as his Qoya a full sister, thus maintaining the purity of the golden solar blood. But he also had at his disposal a great sisterhood of beautiful concubines. These came in the main from the Chosen Women, another most characteristic part of Inca life. At intervals officials inspected the girl children of the land, both noble and common, selected the loveliest and most promising, and sent them to be raised at an Accla Huasi, House of the Chosen Women, which had been set up throughout the Empire. They were in the hands of matrons, the overripe fruit of previous selections, and lived a life that was at once enclosed and luxurious. A few of these girls, and they were promised a blissful afterlife, were dedicated for sacrifice on such special occasions as a victory or the coronation of the Sapa Inca. In the Inca cemetery at Pachacamac excavators found the mummies of several girls who had been richly dressed and honourably buried, but who had died by strangling. One can assume that they had been numbered among this fortunate few, after serving in the great sun temple there.

Others of the selected girls were held in readiness for the Inca to award to favourite nobles and successful soldiers, while the remainder—and they must surely have been the fairest of the fair—were either assigned to the Inca himself to be his concubines and weave his exquisite vicuna robes, or became *Mamacuna*, or Virgins of the Sun. They were vowed to chastity and the service of the temples, and to the tendance of the Sun God's holy fire. With such strangely various futures ahead of the

K   129

Chosen Women, it is greatly to be hoped that the matrons had a sense of the characters and vocations of their young charges.

The Accla Huasi at Cuzco enjoyed the privileges of the royal capital. It is said that all the inmates came from noble families and that there were as many as fifteen hundred of them. Only the Sapa Inca and his immediate family had access to this establishment, where the dwelling-houses and workshops for spinning and weaving were set in delicious gardens with orchards, streams and fountains. The dark, closely masoned walls which cut it off from the outer world still stand, the whole site having been appropriately transferred to a convent of St. Catharine.

Such arrangements as these enabled a vigorous Sapa Inca to have great numbers of children. They were of importance to the state, for they and their descendants made royal kinship groups which formed the ruling nobility. These royal offspring were the true Incas or Children of the Sun. They wore distinctive headdresses and the large, lobe-distorting ear plugs that led the Spaniards to call them Orejones, or Big-ears. As the Empire expanded, the blood royal, copious though it was, could not provide enough men to staff the administration, and a class of Incas by appointment was recruited to fill the middle ranks. The hereditary Children of the Sun were exempted from taxation, and shared with the Sapa Inca himself the right to use the two precious metals—lunar silver and solar gold.

Under this army of civil servants the entire population was divided into units of 100, 500, 1,000, 5,000 and 10,000 heads of families or taxpayers, each presided over by an official of appropriate rank. Above them in size came the provinces and the Four Quarters, ruled by the chief dignitaries of state, and below them little groups of ten and fifty taxpayers which were the responsibility of non-hereditary petty officials. As well as being divided into this mounting series of units based on domicile, the subjects of the Incas were also divided into no less than twelve age groups, each with its special rights and duties.

Taxes were levied in a manner comparable with that of the Sumerians and Babylonians. The cultivated land of every community was divided into three parts, one belonging to the Sapa Inca for his own and state expenses, one to the Sun for religious expenses, and one to the cultivators themselves. In addition there was a levy of men for the army, road-making, mining and other public works, while artisans such as metal workers and weavers had to contribute to the state by the exercise of their skills. When men were drafted away from home the community tilled their land and looked after their families. The women had no more liberty than the men. Their age groups had their own obligations, while for all those who were not taken away to join the Chosen Women, officials found suitable husbands.

In short the people of the Inca Empire lived in perhaps the most extreme form of Welfare State ever successfully established, and one which put more emphasis on duties than on rights. None except the Children of the Sun could be rich, but none was poor either; none could be neglected or forgotten. It seems to us a slavish society, but at least within its limits it functioned well. Communications were probably the best before the modern age; the cultivation of the soil was superb and would have made for stability. The Sapa Inca and the Children of the Sun accepted the fact that their own fortunes depended on the prosperity of their subjects. And it is as well to remember that such records as survive suggest that before the whole intricate structure was overthrown by the Spaniards, the people of this sun kingdom were well content.

Sun worship was unquestionably supreme throughout the Inca Empire, yet the Sun God was not theologically the supreme deity of the pantheon. This was the creator god, best known from the hispanicized version of one of his names as Viracocha, who had made not only the earth and its life but also the other deities. His fate recalls that of other high gods remote from everyday things, especially Anu in Mesopotamia, in that while all men recognized his supremacy none paid him much heed. He had become so excessively elevated that he was perhaps felt to be above doing much for men struggling to raise their crops and their families and pay their taxes. So it was the gods below him in the divine hierarchy who were best served and honoured, the gods of the heavens and the earth, and above all the Sun God, Inti.

Inti had a dual strength. The whole of the original Inca kingdom and a great part of the Empire lay at heights between ten and fifteen thousand feet above the sea. At that height the ripening of maize can be precarious and dependence upon the sun is therefore emphasized. Also, at night, or when the sun is obscured, a shivering chill touches the flesh so that the warmth that comes only directly from the sun seems infinitely precious. It has been claimed that there was a sharp contrast between the people who lived by the sea and worshipped the moon, and the sun-worshippers of the Andes who conquered them. This is an over-simplification yet contains some truth. Although the Children of the Sun came to realize that men suffered if moved between the lofty valleys and the coastal plain and usually tried to keep them at their native altitudes, many officials must have had to move between them. Surely, knowing nothing of the greenhouse effect, they must have been mystified to find the sun so much hotter by the sea than it was when they had climbed back thousands of feet towards it. I should like to know what explanation they devised.

The second source of the Sun God's strength among the Inca peoples, and it may of course converge with the first, was that he was the father of their divine ruler and founder of the kingdom. The fact that their Sapa Inca was called Son of the Sun, and the host of royal offspring regulating their days the Children of the Sun, must have imbued them with a deep sense of solar paternity. He was the Big Father of their Welfare State.

One of the similarities which made the conquering Spaniards believe that Inca religion was a caricature of Christianity devised by the devil was that the confession of sins played an important part in it. The ordinary people confessed to the priest of their local *waca* or shrine, but the heads of state—the Sapa Inca and his family and the High Priest who was always a relative—confessed in secret directly to Inti, apparently seeking his intercession with Viracocha.

Every morning in Cuzco fires were lit from an aromatic wood specially carved to make it pleasing to the god and a priest cast food on to it, saying: 'Eat this, Lord Sun, and acknowledge thy children.' The remainder of the food was then taken and put before the priests for their breakfast. Later in the day a dark chestnut llama was offered in sacrifice.

The four principal festivals of the year were determined by the solar calendar. They celebrated the solstices and equinoxes—and of the four the greatest was the festival held at the summer solstice. Nobles from all over the Empire came into Cuzco, and for three days everyone in the capital fasted and no fires were lit. Then, on the longest day, all gathered in the central plaza dressed in their finest clothes, bright with feathers and flashing with gold and silver. The Sapa Inca poured a libation to the Sun God from a golden vase before leading a procession of the Children of the Sun to the Coricancha temple. Later they re-appeared to make public sacrifices of flowers, grain, gums, llamas—and rarely of a Virgin of the Sun. Perhaps the most sacred moment was when a concave mirror of burnished bronze was held to catch the sun's rays and kindle a bunch of cotton. The fire thus renewed by the Sun God at the time of his greatest strength was then used to make burnt offerings on the altars, and was handed over to the Virgins of the Sun to be jealously guarded and maintained through the coming year. The people were given an abundant feast of llama meat, a rare indulgence. If the day of the solstice was clouded and the fire had to be lit by friction there was grave anxiety for the seasons ahead. If the Virgins had allowed it to go out the dangers would have been even greater—but if they ever did they kept it from knowledge and the pages of history.

Cuzco, where this and so many other royal and holy occasions were celebrated, presented a great contrast with that other capital city of the sun—Akhetaten. While the city by the Nile was run up rather flimsily, poorly built walls being masked by plaster and beguilingly painted, the city in the high Andes, begun some two and a half millennia later, was probably the most solidly constructed in the world. In recent times when earthquakes have wrecked the Spanish and later buildings, the ponderous Incaic walls have stood almost unshaken. These walls were often built in andesite, an igneous rock, some by the extraordinary technique of shaping the blocks into irregular polygonal forms, as various in size as in number of sides (one famous block in Cuzco has twelve), and fitting them together like a gigantic cubist jigsaw. Others were raised in regular courses with the joints sunk as in our eighteenth-century rusticated masonry, and fitted so that there is hardly a hair's-breadth between block and block.

Although when viewed from the slopes above, Cuzco looks like a Spanish city, with its wide-eaved roofs of mellow tiles, its balconies, arcaded plazas, church towers and domes, anyone walking the streets can feel he is in the Inca capital. This is because in so many places the Incaic walls stand to a height of ten feet or more, but are crowned with later buildings. One of the most impressive of the surviving streets is the Calle de Loreto, formerly the Inty-kjicllu or Lane of the Sun. It runs like a narrow ravine between the dark, almost featureless walls of the Palace of the Sapa Inca, Huayna-Capac, on one side, and of the House of the Chosen Women on the other. Could Akhenaten have been a visitor, he would almost certainly have been as out of love with this harsh, stony city as with the ideas and practices of his fellow Son of the Sun.

Yet in imagining the place as it must have been in the decades of its glory immediately before the Spanish Conquest, one has to remember that although the narrow streets were severe, the men, women and children using them probably introduced an abundance of colour. Today, in spite of poverty, their descendants weave clothes of great brilliance, a sumptuous red usually predominating. When they gather together the effect is like a glowing fire. In ancient Cuzco, where there were so many priests and nobles, yet more gorgeous clothing, enhanced with precious metals and tropical feathers, must have lit up streets and squares. Indeed the contrast of richness and austerity, of colour set off by darkness, would have made a challenge to the European painters of the age.

It seems to have been usual for each succeeding Sapa Inca to build himself a new palace, the previous one becoming a kind of shrine or museum commemorating its owner. So the capital became a cluster of palaces, interspersed with plazas, temples and buildings devoted to science and learning, and dominated by the fortress, like a stone-built and cyclopean Maiden Castle, built by Pachacuti on a precipitous hill above the town. The main square, now the Plaza de Armas, was known as the Place of Weeping. In the centre was a raised dais where the Sapa Inca, his family and leading subjects sat enthroned during the seasonal festivals. From this Place of Weeping it was possible to see the sun columns or gnomons raised on the hills to the east and west. According to some records these were used to measure the solstices and equinox—which seems not at all improbable. But now it is thought that they were only markers indicating the agricultural seasons by the position of the rising and setting of the sun behind the mountains.

The building which is of surpassing interest here, which indeed comes at once to mind if one is thinking of man's greatest tributes to the sun, is the Coricancha, or Place of Gold, usually called the Temple of the Sun. Although it is true that Viracocha officially held the chief place in it, this popular name probably reflects the actual state of affairs prevailing. In the chief temple of the Sapa Inca's own capital, a city which was essentially the royal seat of the Son of the Sun, the solar cult must have predominated. In addition to the Sun Temple itself, the Coricancha consisted of a number of separate sanctuaries dedicated to other celestial divinities, one to the moon, to Venus, to the stars, to thunder and lightning and to the rainbow, set within a precinct wall.

From the moment of its discovery, and inevitable pillage by the Spaniards, the fame of the Sun Temple at Cuzco spread throughout the civilized world. The doors were gold-sheathed, and on the western wall was a rayed sun disk embossed on a jewel-studded plaque so arranged that the rays of sunrise fell upon it and filled the temple with a strange reflected light. The moon sanctuary had a similar disk in silver. According to some records the Coricancha also contained a golden garden, an eldorado of charming fantasy. Trees, flowers and birds were all of gold, and a life-sized golden herdsman tended his golden llamas. Butterflies of gold leaf, light enough to float on a breeze, hovered above the flowers.

The Son of the Sun must often have come to this temple, those seeing him perhaps redoubling the normal ceremonial abasement which demanded that all should appear as though stooped by a burden, should bare their feet and keep their eyes downcast in the presence of their divine Emperor. According to some ancient accounts, the Sapa Inca returned to the Coricancha when at last he had been 'called home to the sun'. The mummified body, richly clad, of each successive Sapa Inca was seated in a golden throne with that of his Qoya opposite to him, until at last a line of kings faced a line of queens with the great golden sun disk glittering above their withered flesh.

In another version, however, the royal corpses were seated not in the Sun Temple but in their own palaces, where the life of the household continued as though they were still alive. This convention seems far more agreeable than that of placing dead servants in a tomb. Whichever the last resting-place of the Sons of the Sun, there is no doubt that at high festivals their mummies were taken out and carried in procession about the city, just as later under the Spanish the effigies of saints or of the Virgin were taken from the churches.

Today there is nothing left of the riches and fantasy of the Coricancha. It was taken over for a Dominican friary, and the Intypampa or Plaza of the Sun where liturgical dances were performed is now the Plazoleta de Santo Domingo. Yet much of the astonishingly perfect masonry still stands. Indeed, when I saw it, while the perfect ashlar of the famous apsidal end of the Sun Temple showed only the slightest mark of the shock of the recent earthquake, the church of Santo Domingo built upon it was in tattered ruin. No wonder, for the Incaic building, everywhere of extraordinary strength, is here at its best. The blocks, worked without metal in the hard andesite, have their upper surfaces slightly concave and their lower ones convex so that the mortarless joints are powerfully tenacious. Those who worked for the Intip Cori and his father the sun certainly worked well.

Of all the signs of the former worship of the Sun God that one sees in Peru, the one which struck my imagination most deeply was the gnomon at Machu Picchu. These pointers, with four irregular sides, were set up, sometimes within a circle, in many sun temples. They were sundials for reading not the hours but the seasons. When, near midsummer, the gnomon cast almost no shadow at noon, it was said that 'the god sat with all his light upon the column'. It seems that Quito was especially honoured because, as it lies on the equator, there most clearly of all the god was upon the column. But in situation Quito's solar observatory surely could not compare with Machu Picchu's.

By good fortune I have been able to see many of the most marvellous remains of the human past throughout the world. For its natural setting the little city of Machu Picchu far surpasses them all. It is almost complete, almost as it was when administered by the Children of the Sun. The military walls and round tower, the houses and many temples and other ceremonial buildings, the flights of thousands of steps which form the steep streets, the conduits of bright mountain water, are all as they were made. Only the roofs, probably of ornately cut thatch, have disappeared. Yet it is not this human handi-work, exceptional though it is, that gives Machu Picchu its overwhelming greatness; it is nature.

The town is built on a rock spur about a thousand feet above the valley, which is itself nine thousand feet above the sea. On the approach side (though this is in places precipitous) it is delimited by a massive wall. The other sides are terraced with astonishing skill before they drop into sheer precipices that fall straight to where the River Vilcanota sweeps round in a bold horseshoe. This whole spur, with its green valley skirt and city crown, is enclosed by a vast cirque of rock peaks decked with slender waterfalls. The rock seems peculiarly smooth and many-faceted, so that these fangs glitter like cut jet. Behind them rise the white, sharp summits of the Andean giants, pointing nine-teen and twenty thousand feet towards the sun, and bathed in the stillness of eternal snows.

This mountain landscape is one of austere, almost harsh beauty, yet flavouring it in the imagination is the knowledge that already Machu Picchu is over the watershed, that the Vilcanota flows ultimately into the Amazon and that only a short distance away where the "eyebrow of the jungle" is raised against the mountain chain there is all the lushness of tropical vegetation, the brilliance of its birds and butterflies.

The stepped streets, some of them cut into the native rock, lead one up by straight and angular ways to the highest point in the city, and here at the apex is the Intihuatana, the solar observatory, with the gnomon stone in the centre of an open terrace. This irregular quadrilateral block stands on a solid rock-cut platform, itself hewn into irregular planes and angles, the whole having the air of an enigmatic work of abstract art. I do not think that anybody has tried to discover how the priest astronomers of the Children of the Sun read the shadow of the gnomon as it moved round the platform, but, there on that lofty man-made terrace among the wild peaks, they and their lives seemed very near. I sat on the edge of the platform watching the shadow which they had watched, and a butterfly, probably wafted up from the fields below, tilted round me on its wide and gaudy wings. It was then that I decided I must attempt the book about Man and the Sun which I had long been turning over in my mind.

A popular story of the last days of the Inca capital tells how the great golden sun disk from the Coricancha having been awarded as booty to a Spanish officer, this representative of the conquering Christian faith, caught up in the recklessness that goes with the pillage of a foreign city, gambled away his prize in the course of one night. This, it is said, explains the origin of the Spanish proverb 'To gamble away the sun before morning'. While it is very likely that the story was contrived to explain the saying, it still makes an effective curtain to one of the most remarkable developments of solar religion in our history. Perhaps nowhere else and at no other time was a whole empire so closely knit in worship of the sun and vassalage to his divine and royal counterpart on earth.

While Inti was primarily worshipped as the source of light and of life, that other aspect of the Sun God, his power as the centre of order and justice, must have assumed a distinctive form. On the side of order there was an unusual geographical element. The Four Quarters of the Empire met at the Coricancha and it seems that the local temples and shrines were built along lines subdividing these quarters—perhaps intended to represent the sun's rays emanating throughout the land from the supreme Sun Temple. Then the 'all-seeing eye' concept of solar justice was evidently weakened in this totalitarian and communistical state. As there were no money, no capitalists, practically no private property and no codified laws, courts of law as they grew up in the Old World were unknown. There were regulations and punishments administered much as in a school, with the Sapa Inca as the ultimate authority. It was only in this authoritarian or paternalistic sense that Inti was concerned with justice.

Yet the empire of the Children of the Sun was one of exceptionally good order—of that there can be no doubt. It was also one of reasonable light, even if entirely lacking in anything to compare with the spiritual illumination of an Akhenaten. In both these virtues it contrasted with the states of other sun-worshipping American peoples living on the north side of the equator. There ultimately the reverse side of the Sun God, one never otherwise known, made his brief and dire emergence from the mind of man—a divinity of disorder and darkness.

The civilization of the Maya was probably the first in the New World to deserve the name; for its remarkable feats in astronomy and mathematics, its achievement of hieroglyphic writing and the quality of its best architecture and sculpture it can also claim to be the greatest. The status of the Sun God within it has none of the obvious pre-eminence granted to Inti, yet there is a good deal to suggest that he was in fact the leading divinity. Whatever his theological position, he could not have attained the same power, for the Maya, who lived in what is now southern Honduras, Guatemala and Yucatan, never created a centralized empire but a loose federation of city states.

It may be that when the heart of Maya civilization shifted sharply from the northern foothills of the Peten where rain was plentiful to the much drier country of the Yucatan peninsula, the Chacs or rain gods gained greatly in importance and popularity. Certainly as one walks among the huge and impressive ruins of such places as Chichen Itza and Uxmal, the stylized heads of the Chacs thrusting out from the walls are far more conspicuous than the sun disks. More conspicuous still is the sinuous body and sinister tail-rattle of the feathered serpent, the god Quetzalcoatl—but he, as will appear, was an intruder from the Mexican plateau.

It seems in itself probable that in the heydays of the Classic Maya culture, between the third and the ninth centuries A.D., the celestial divinities were supreme. For this was the age when the Maya became obsessed with the measurement of time, deifying the days, months and years and losing themselves in immense calendrical and astronomical calculations that were part religious and mystical, part practical and even scientific. Indeed, it may well be that this first and greatest phase of Maya civilization was brought to an end by a peasants' revolt against an élite who were felt to have their heads so high among the stars that they were neglecting the earthly matters of fields and crops. And there is no doubt that among the heavenly divinities with whose movements they became obsessed, as they established one of the most accurate calendars the world has ever known and worked out dates millions of years into the past, the most important were the sun, the moon and the planet Venus.

An indication of the supreme importance of the Sun God can be found in the name for a priest which was Ah Kin, He of the Sun, while the chief priest was the Ah Kin Mai or Ahau Kin Mai. Again, while, like our own, all the day names were those of gods, the day name of Ahau, the Sun God, was of particular importance. The most significant span of time for the Maya was the katun equalling twenty tun, or a little less than twenty years, and their calendar was so devised that a katun could end only on one of the Ahau or Sun-days. The days were further distinguished by numbers up to thirteen, and it therefore took a cycle of thirteen katuns or 260 tuns to run through all the Ahau days and start a fresh cycle. Each katun was named after its last day—as though a year were not called, for example, 1961, but Sunday 31 year, but while it is only a chance that I am writing in a year that ends on a Sunday, among the Maya it would inevitably have been so. Furthermore, as it was held that the patterns of history were repeated in each cycle of thirteen katuns, and this was the basis of divinations and the reading of auspicious and inauspicious periods, this cycle related to the Sun-days was of the greatest importance.

These facts strongly suggest the dominance of the Sun God in the religion of the Classic period of which so little is directly known. All chronicles and histories both native and Spanish date from the time when the Classic epoch and its calendar cult were at an end, and when the Maya had been influenced by conquest and infiltration by the Toltecs from the Valley of Mexico. It is of interest here because it shows how the ruling class of one American civilization followed ways decidedly different from the rest and became interested in the sun from the point of view of time and exact measurement. It was not essentially a scientific approach, for their views of time were religious, yet it led to a detached observation which enabled mathematically-minded priests to construct a table for predicting the periods when eclipses of the sun may occur. Also their immense calculations back into the past not only led them to discover the use of the zero (considerably before it was discovered in the Old World) but also encouraged them to dwell on truly vast spans of time. Thus a stela at Quiriga records an exact calendrical computation for a date four hundred million years ago—a vision much more appropriate to solar history as we now know it than the puny dates for the creation of the world accepted by most peoples until modern times. In short, while it would be false to claim a true beginning of the Apollonian mind which we shall find among the Greeks, something of its spirit existed among the intellectual élite of the Maya priesthood.

While it seems probable that on the one hand some of the thinkers may have become totally preoccupied with the pleasures of mathematics and impatient of their priestly functions, on the other the mass of the people had no very exalted view of the celestial divinities. Among the Inca the Moon Goddess appears to have been generally accepted as the sister-wife of Inti, but no great importance is known to have been attached to the relationship. Among the Maya the Sun God and Moon Goddess had as irregular marital relations as any of the Olympians. The Sun, a famous hunter and patron of poetry and music, and the Moon, Goddess of weaving and childbirth, and perhaps also of maize, had been the first inhabitants of the world, and also the first to couple. The goddess, however, was an unfaithful wife and she came to be identified with sexual indulgence. The blossom of the frangipani, and the monkey, were both symbols of sexual intercourse and came to be identified with the sun and moon. When the two deities left the earth to reign in the sky the moon shone less brightly than the sun because the god had pulled out one of her eyes in a tussle. The heavenly pair were addressed by such titles as lord and lady, our father and our mother, our grandfather and our grandmother.

While the Sun God belonged essentially to the sky, his night journey below the earth made him one of the lords of the underworld—very much as he was in Egypt. When he emerged at sunrise he had to be shown with the insignia of death. In his underworld aspect he also had the colour black and the jaguar as his attributes.

It may be that this underworld aspect of the Sun God was developed only after the Toltec influx which I have already mentioned. Among the Toltecs and the later Aztecs as will soon appear, it was of great significance, and the vision of the Sun God emerging as a skeleton from the underworld was among these peoples one of the reasons why he had to be revived and nourished with human lives. Much has been written of the contrast between the gentle Maya of the early days of the Classic culture and their warlike and bloodstained neighbours who later corrupted them. There is some truth in the picture. Even after the coming of the Toltecs, they never allowed the lust for sacrifice to take full possession of them, and in earlier days human sacrifice may have been rare. Nevertheless sculpture of the Classic period is full of brutal pictures of the humiliation of prisoners of war, and in the amazing eighth-century mural paintings at Bonampak there are some very nasty scenes indeed. Still, it remains true that it was the peoples of the Valley of Mexico who allowed rites which at first were of a kind quite usual among peoples at their stage of development so to take hold of them, so to permeate the psyche and release its darkest desires, that their religion became an abomination and warfare a chronic disease. I intend, then, to leave the Maya and to follow this darkest passage in the relationship between man and the sun as it was enacted among the Toltecs and their successors.

The history of the Valley of Mexico, and particularly that part of it in the region of the great lakes Texcoco and Chalco which have dried up since the days of the Spanish Conquest, is complicated, little understood—and quite extraordinary. Of actual historical events I do not want to say much. One among the many simple farming peoples established there in the early centuries of our era developed the amazing civilization associated with Teotihuacan, their city on the east side of Lake Texcoco. They came to be known as Toltecs, or Master Builders, but this proud title was also adopted by other groups just as the barbarian invaders claimed to belong to a Holy Roman Empire. They began to create their city in the sixth century and brought it to its full magnificence in the next three hundred years. So that although, so far as we know, the contact between them was of the slightest, this people in the Valley of Mexico and the Maya in the jungles of Guatemala flourished at the same time. Both put extraordinary energy into fufilling the religious imagination, both built stepped and temple-crowned pyramids and both directed their lives according to a holy calendar. But whereas the Mayan élite became more and more absorbed with time, its measurement and meaning, and can be said to have been devoted to the celestial divinities mainly from this point of view, the Toltec thinkers seem to have become interested in ideas of union with the great ones of the heavens. Both peoples, of course, at the same time served the gods and goddesses of earth and sky in the hope of securing fertility and well-being.

The aspect of the religious imagination developed by the Toltecs proved to be most dangerous among peoples who had not slowly created a civilization, but had seized upon one ready made and adapted it to the habits and values of their recent barbarism. Teotihuacan was probably abandoned in the tenth or eleventh century, at about the time when, as has been seen, Toltecs were pushing into the Maya territory. The collapse of their great ceremonial capital may have been partly caused by its own excess—by demands upon labour, food and other raw materials beyond what the country could yield or the people endure. But it was also brought about by the invasion of the Valley of Mexico by various unsettled tribes in search of land. Where it was vacant these Chichimecas settled peacefully; where it belonged to the Toltecs or others, they fought for it. Soon the Valley was divided into a number of petty states, usually centred on a city, all much devoted to internecine war and intrigue. One of the strongest was Culhuacan to the south of Lake Texcoco, and in the middle of the thirteenth century a dynasty appeared there which seems to have introduced a new cultural tradition derived from the Pueblo region away to the south-east. This was the beginning of what can be called Aztec civilization. It spread through the valley, although, as the conditions of the time made inevitable, there was variation from state to state according to the tradition of the tribe and the surviving influence from the Toltec past.

Aztec civilization, in fact, meant nothing very coherent while power and the fortunes of war shifted from city to city. Among the many peoples of the Valley were the Tenochas, who seem to have slipped quietly in by the north of the Lake and settled at Chapultepec near its south-west corner. Their tribal legends told how before this they had left their original cave dwellings, found the image of their god Huitzilopochtli, and carried it with them on their wanderings. He gave them directions, and often led the way in the form of a humming-bird. At Chapultapec their aggressiveness led them to provoke their more powerful neighbours, and in their defeat some were forced into serfdom under the victorious chief of Culhuacan, while others fled to take refuge on swampy and unhealthy islands just off the shore of the lake. With the changing fortunes of war, the Tenochas of the islands grew stronger, won land on the mainland and were joined by their kinsmen from Cul-huacan who by now were in possession of the ways of Aztec civilization.

With the fifteenth century the once subject Tenochas became the most powerful of the Aztec peoples of the Valley of Mexico, conquering their neighbours and peoples far beyond them. The island fastness, where they had lived so miserably as refugees, they built up into the superb city of Tenochtitlan, the capital of Montezuma, which so dazzled the Spaniards when first they saw it. The great ceremonial square created by the Tenocha Aztecs became the main plaza of the Spanish capital of Mexico, and is now the main plaza of Mexico City.

It is curious that all unknown to one another the Tenocha Aztecs and the Incas enjoyed their time of conquest and dominance simultaneously. But while the Incas annexed terri-tory peacefully when they could and knit each subject people into their unified empire, the Aztecs had no imperial organiza-tion but merely exercised a chaotic martial hegemony, exacting tribute in treasure and carrying off prisoners for sacrifice. It is hardly surprising, then, that while the Sun God of the Incas became a generally benevolent paternalistic deity, with the Aztecs he developed an insatiable appetite for human sacrifice, his worship thus both depending upon, and necessitating, ceaseless war.

I have said that it is not surprising, yet looked at afresh it is profoundly astonishing that men and women just like our-selves, with the same capacity for personal love and grief,

146

should have built up a society and a religion which applauded the cutting out of the hearts of countless fellow creatures, which maintained temples crusted with blood and, in the heart of a city of beauty and dignity, a huge rack crammed with innumerable spitted human skulls. These things were done in the name of the Sun God, just as the Inquisition tortured and burnt in the name of the God of Love.

Ruth Benedict has written of the great arc of possible human behaviour from which each culture must select one segment to develop at the expense of the rest. The segment selected and developed to the extreme by the Aztecs was projected from the darkest quarter of the human psyche. I want to discover how this came to pass, there in the bright thin air of the Valley of Mexico. How in a land where worship of the Sun God helped men to a creative energy as remarkable as any in the world, a religion of life and light should have become corrupted to its opposite.

It is as difficult to separate Toltec religion from that of the Aztecs as it is to distinguish Classic Maya religion and that which prevailed after the Mexican infiltration. In both cases it was only the latest forms which were more or less adequately recorded under Spanish rule. However, the invading barbarians who finally created Aztec civilization insisted that they took their culture from their predecessors, and this is very largely borne out by the evidence of pre-Toltec remains and especially those of their astounding city of Teotihuacan. The religious history of the two peoples must be treated as continuous.

Among the Toltecs we meet again a situation which has become familiar, but which remains elusive and difficult to explain. Theologically the Sun God was not clearly supreme and yet his worship was absolutely dominant. They possessed one of the somewhat neglected high gods in Tloque Nahuaque; a rain and a fire god and an earth goddess seem to have been ancient and important, and a frog goddess had a rich temple in the capital. And there was Quetzalcoatl, the divinity symbolized by the famous feathered serpent. He had, or came to have, very many aspects. Perhaps among the Toltecs he was primarily a culture hero, a god of civilization who had brought the Master Builders all their knowledge and skills. It was probably in this aspect that he gave his name to the high priests, who still in Aztec times were entitled Quetzalcoatl. But he was also in time a wind god, with a wind god's tendency to be exalted into the life of the spirit. Again he appeared in some myths as a god of extreme purity and one who could be seen as a redeemer giving his blood for the life of men. Having been famed among the other gods for his absolute sexual continence and sobriety, he was induced by them to make himself drunk and to fornicate. He was then so guilt-stricken by his fall into sin that he sacrificed himself by burning, and his soul ascended as Venus to seek final union with the sun. The fact that the people of Mexico had a very good view of Venus as evening star disappearing for a spell into the underworld and then reappearing in the east as a morning star with the sun, had a powerful effect on their mythopoeic thought. An idea of all human souls being redeemed by returning to the sun from whence they had come seems indeed to have underlain the cruder ideas of both Aztecs and Toltecs. An Aztec poem of considerable power expresses the idea:

> *I offer, offer flowering cocoa*
> *That I may be sent to the House of the Sun!*
> *Beautiful and very rich is the crown of quetzal plumes:*
> *May I know the House of the Sun, may I go to that place!*
> *Oh, no one contains in his soul the lovely inebriate flower:*
> *Each time the sun climbs this mountain*
> *My heart cries and is sad:*
> *Would it were the flower of my heart painted in beautiful colours!*
> *The King of those who return sings of the flowers!*

This concept of the sun as the King of those who return, that is the being from whom souls come and to whom they are reunited, may help to explain the overriding importance of the star even among the Toltecs for whom Quetzalcoatl and other divinities seem to have had a higher status within the pantheon.

The majestic ruins at Teotihuacan leave no doubt of the overwhelming importance of sun worship among the Toltecs. Between the seventh and ninth centuries, they built a capital which dwarfed most of the Wonders of our Old World. Along a ceremonial street running north and south they constructed a line of huge precincts or walled plazas, each one framing a terraced platform or a pyramid supporting a temple on its summit. To the extreme south lay the Temple of Quetzalcoatl, the platform carved with a composition of feathered serpents and rain-god masks that is one of the most ferocious and awe-inspiring sculptural creations ever made. Yet in size this sanctuary did not compare with those at the northern end of the sacred way, the temples of the sun and moon. The Moon Temple to the north stood on a large truncated pyramid approached through a court and climbed by a broad staircase on the southern side; it was large, but looked modest beside the Pyramid of the Sun. This, built of adobe taken from the demolition of older buildings, and faced with stone, had sides seven hundred feet long at the base (only a little less than those of the Great Pyramid by the Nile) and rose in four terraces to a height of over two hundred feet. From the temple on the summit the priests would have been able to see far over the gently undulating country, surveying the fields of maize and squash and beans of the peasants whose devout toil supported them and their colossal projects. There is no need to doubt that at this time all alike were equally convinced that without the priests and their works crops would have failed, the sun stood still, the holy calendar ceased to revolve and man have perished.

Did sacrificial victims climb that seemingly endless flight of steep and narrow stairs up to this lofty Temple of the Sun? Remembering that already in their Classic period the Maya occasionally practised human sacrifice, and that this greatly increased with the Toltec influence in later times, it seems

almost certain that the answer is yes. But it is probably also fair
to assume that it was still kept within bounds and that it was
carried out with a ritual dignity and religious intensity of feeling
that would redeem it from the brutal horror of Aztec practice.
In fact it is likely that the annual sacrifice to the god Tezcatlipoca which was still being enacted in the Aztec capital at the
time of the Spanish Conquest represented a survival of the kind
of rite that may have been enacted on the Sun Pyramid at
Teotihuacan. If one can stomach the idea of human sacrifice,
then this enactment has a certain moving pathos. A handsome,
brave and unblemished prisoner of war was chosen (perhaps
among the Toltecs it may have been one of their own warriors).
He was given eight pages to wait upon him, and taught by the
priests the habits of speech and manners of the court. He was
also taught how to play sacred music on the flute. Everywhere
as he went through the streets playing his instrument the people
worshipped him and kissed the ground where he trod—for
while he lived out the course of a year he was the true embodiment of the god. Then, twenty days before the end of his year,
four maidens specially reared for the purpose and named after
goddesses came to attend him and make love with him as the
hour of his doom approached. Five days before the end he
attained the height of godhead; the king himself stayed within
doors and all the court followed the young Tezcatlipoca, allowing him to pass days and nights in a dream of banqueting and
ritual dancing, everyone in splendid ceremonial dress and worshipping before him. Then came the break. He was put in a
royal boat with his four brides and taken to a 'little hill 'apart;
here all his gorgeous following and the goddesses themselves
had to stay behind, leaving him to go on attended only by his
pages. They made their way to a humble and isolated temple,
and there the young man with his burden of divinity had to
leave the last of his fellows, climbing slowly up the pyramid
quite alone. At each stage of the ascent he ritually broke one of
the flutes on which he had played the sacred melodies during

the past year; as he mounted the pipes fell down the steps behind him.

When he had come to the top, to the highest part of the temple, there were the priests who were to kill him, standing in pairs, and they took him and bound his head and hands, lying him upon his back upon the block. He that had the stone knife plunged it into his breast with a great thrust, and drawing it forth, put his hand into the incision the knife had made, and pulled out the heart and offered it at once to the sun.

Tezcatlipoca was the Sun God in one of his aspects, and it seems that this whole ritual year was an enactment of the solar cycle, the last twenty days perhaps representing the time of the winter solstice, and the four goddesses the earth trying to hold back the sun. The final sacrifice would then symbolize the sun's escape—and indeed further rites which immediately followed seem to have represented the return of the Day Sun, the resurrection of the year.

It may seem hardly warranted to transfer this rite, which certainly was celebrated by the Aztecs down to their last years of independence, to the Toltecs of Teotihuacan. Yet it does suggest a more truly religious and less martial tradition. Its celebration, too, can still be reconciled with high priests each of whom was chosen because he was 'virtuous, humble and peace-loving . . . affectionate, merciful and compassionate, a friend of all, devout and fearful of god'.

Behind the Toltec and Aztec pantheon and its myths were three cosmological theories which permeated their whole religious outlook. The first was the theory of opposites, that light fought against dark, sin against virtue, and so forth. This was, of course, extended to the gods representing these opposites. Thus Quetzalcoatl fought against Tezcatlipoca, the Eagle Knights of Day against the Jaguar Knights of Darkness. The next theory was that before the creation of the present sun and its world, four others had existed and been destroyed. In turn

151

each of the great gods and goddesses had assumed the role of the sun: Tezcatlipoca, Quetzalcoatl, Tlaloc, and Chalchiuhtlicue the water goddess. Yet each world and its sun was destroyed by powers associated with the god who was the sun—by jaguars and darkness, by wind, by fiery rain, by floods. The present sun was sometimes called the sun of movement, and its god was Tonatiuh; it was fated to be destroyed by earthquakes.

This cosmic history helps to show that whatever the order of the pantheon, the sun was so fully accepted as the very heart and essence of the world that any of the greater gods could assume the sun's part. The five suns, four dead and one living, are related to the third cosmic principle. This is one already familiar from other American peoples—the division of the world into four quarters about the central zenith and nadir. Among the Aztecs it was as important as among the Incas, although lacking the exact geographical significance only possible within a unified empire. All plants and animals and birds were assigned to the directions, so too were the four divisions of the sacred calendar, and from that men and women according to their birthdays. Gods also had their quarters, or might belong to all four of them according to their different aspects. As a symbol the four points set about a central one stood for the sun's heat, and also the five suns of the cosmic eras.

The way in which all these images coalesced is displayed on the great Calendar Stone, once one of the most sacred objects in Tenochtitlan and now a treasure of the National Museum of Mexico. This massive stone disk, thirteen feet across, is at once a total picture of the being of the sun and a symbolic expression of the history of the world. In a central ring is framed the face of Tonatiuh, known as 'the shining one' and 'the eagle that soars'; at each side of the ring his hands, sharp with eagle claws, grip human hearts. The frame around this centre is the sign for the date 4 Earthquake, the day on which the present sun is to be destroyed, while filling the four squares of the sign are pictograms for the four past suns. Round this again are ringed the

V. AZTEC CALENDAR STONE

day signs, then rings bearing solar rays and jewels. The whole intricate design is encircled by the bodies of two fire serpents, used by the sun to fight his holy war with his enemies of the might. This Calendar Stone, which ranks with the Egyptian obelisks among the most famous solar symbols of mankind, leads to the very heart of the Aztec world, to fifteenth-century Tenochtitlan when the Tenochas were at the height of their power.

I do not want to set out the Aztec pantheon and its mythology. Like the Egyptian, it is confused by elements drawn from the past, from different peoples and different cities. And without an adequate writing system, a unified empire or sufficient time, it was impossible for the priests to have formulated an agreed theology; when the Conquest came to end it, Aztec religion was still in a state of flux. If one had been able to climb to the Great Temple and question the Chief Priest across his own altar, he would not have been able to explain the difficulties and complexities of his faith and practice. He might, perhaps, have been able to show that there was a tendency to syncretize many of the old gods. He would have made it plain that there were more spiritual ideas in sun worship than the notion of feeding a solar warrior, quoting such literature as the hymn I have already quoted and describing the communion rite in which the body of Huitzilopochtli was shaped in corn flour and then divided throughout the kingdom. Nevertheless, what would have emerged most strongly from any high priest would have been his faith in the greatness of the Aztec Sun God and the service his people was doing the whole world in fighting his battle.

For this is what is most essential in the meaning of the Aztecs' history. They were the chosen people of the Sun God, bound to fulfil a divine destiny. In the national myth inspiring them, Huitzilopochtli had given instructions that they were to wander until they saw an eagle alight on a cactus with fruits red like human hearts. It would be Huitztlampa, the Land of the

Sun, and there they were to settle, conquer and grow great. Then, the god told them:

This first thing to adorn thee shall be the order of the eagle, the order of the jaguar, the sacred war, arrow and shield; this is what thou shalt eat and what thou shalt be needing; and so thou shalt go striking terror. As a reward for thy valour thou shalt conquer and destroy all the plebeians and settlers already established there . . .

and on another occasion he declared to them:

Behold, Mexicans, here is your duty and your vocation, here you are to watch and wait, and from all four corners of the earth you are to conquer, earn and subdue for yourselves. Have then body, breast, head, arms and strength, for it will cost much sweat, work and pure blood . . .

So the Tenochas were led through the wilderness by their god and promised unbounding dominion in his name. The eagle lighted on the cactus on the island in the Lake of the Moon (the esoteric title for Lake Texcoco), and there they built Tenochtitlan and fulfilled their destiny.

Huitzilopochtli was probably the only god in their pantheon who belonged exclusively to the Aztecs. He was in fact the tribal god of a migrating people who had come to be god of their city. When he had to find his place in the wider heavens of the Toltec pantheon he was recognized as the sun of the blue sky of day in opposition to Tezcatlipoca the sun of the night and underworld. One of his symbols was the high-soaring eagle of the daylight hours, just as the night-haunting jaguar stood for Tezcatlipoca. The humming-birds, whose plumage, refracting the rays of the sun, seemed to flash and burn, represented Huitzilopochtli at the zenith. It was in this form that the god led the Tenochas in their migrations. It may be that emeralds and turquoise were regarded a gems of the sun not only for their own brilliance but because they suggested the plumage of many of these most exquisite little birds.

The third and least important of the Sun God trinity was Tonatiuh, the existing sun whose face we have already seen at the centre of the Calendar Stone and who was often represented in this fashion by a disk with a human face. He might, perhaps, be likened to the Aten of the Egyptians before he was exalted by Akhenaten. Indeed, although there are striking differences, particularly the acceptance of a distinct and powerful god of the night sun, it is impossible not to be reminded of the sun world of the Egyptians. There is the same deification of different aspects and different phases of the sun—we think of Re, Khepri, Horus as well as the Aten—the same concepts of solar birds, of a solar contest with the powers of darkness, of the soul's union with the sun. Why, then, was the religious temper and practice attendant on these ideas so different?

This can be answered in two ways, one from the outer world of religious and social forms and of history, the other from the inner world of individual and group psychology. In the outer world the main cause was surely the Aztecs' obsession with contest. As a Mexican apologist for Huitzilopochtli has said, he 'was the sun, the young warrior, born each morning from the womb of the old goddess of the earth, and dying again each evening to illuminate with his dying light the world of the dead'. In one of the migration myths the god himself is made to express this more brutally: 'My principal purpose in coming and my vocation is war . . .' In the leading myth about the birth of Huitzilopochtli, his mother the Earth Goddess Coatlicue had already borne the celestial beings of the night—the moon and all the constellations of the stars—and had retired to live in holy chastity. Finding that she had miraculously conceived, her night children were so angry that they armed to kill her, but when she wept the child in her womb promised to save her. So he did, for at the moment the moon and stars came to kill his mother he leapt forth and with the serpent of fire, the sun's ray, beheaded the moon and put the stars to flight. In another still grimmer myth, after the destruction of the fourth sun, the gods gathered at Teotihuacan to create a new one. Two of them burnt themselves, and the sun and moon rose from the fire, but the sun hung at the horizon declaring that he would not move unless the other gods were sacrificed to him. Venus took an arrow and shot it at the sun, but he caught it and killed her with it, then one by one all the other stars until not one remained alive.

Evidently, then, the idea of the sun's battling with the gods of the night obsessed the Aztec mind far more than the Egyptian. And from war and sacrifice among the gods, the priests would have argued, came the necessity for war and sacrifice among men. The sun was worn out from his struggle—that is why artists sometimes depicted him as a skeleton at sunrise—and had to be restored with human blood—blood representing the essence of life itself. The Aztecs, convinced that they were the chosen people of Huitzilopochtli, saw themselves dedicated to supply him with this essence so that he might continue to bring light and life to the world and to man. They had also to satisfy all the other gods, especially those of rain and of fire, but the needs of the sun were supreme.

To carry out these sacred obligations, the Aztecs had to make themselves into a warrior people. All young men of whatever station were educated for warfare, and unflinching courage and scorn of pain were the highest virtues. The finest warriors were chosen for the honour of belonging either to the Eagle Knights or the Jaguar Knights, the guards regiments, as it were, of the Day Sun and the Night Sun.

The wars launched by this martial people were in large part wars of conquest as has been seen, but they were also waged to provide prisoners for the stones of sacrifice. As the Tenochas rose to absolute power in the Aztec world, they developed the unique and horrifying concept of a form of holy war fought solely to feed the gods. They called it the 'blossoming war' and surrounded it with pious elaborations. It rose to its highest pitch of artificiality in the Tenochas' relationship with the neighbouring people of Tlaxcala, with whom they conducted organized battles which were in fact tourneys fought not between individuals but between peoples. They were battles that the Aztecs had to win, that had to end in many more quivering hearts being raised towards the sun.

Even when the prisoners had been taken, the idea of the sacred combat might be prolonged. The day 4 Earthquake, standing for the present age and the fifth sun, was dedicated to the god Tonatiuh. In the morning a captive had his heart cut out on the stone on the temple pyramid in the usual fashion, and the people feasted while gashing themselves with obsidian knives. Then in the afternoon the Eagle and Jaguar Knights performed dances representing the solar struggle, culminating in a gladiatorial sacrifice. A captive of high military reputation was stood upon a circular stone signifying the sun disk, and was tethered to it with a rope passing round his waist. He was armed with a sword, but one which had only feathers in place of the obsidian blades that edged the true fighting weapon, and was also given four pinewood staves. He was then challenged in single combat by two Eagle Knights and two Jaguar Knights. If by extraordinary prowess he succeeded in repulsing all four, then a fifth, left-handed, Knight would challenge him and (as though by ritual agreement) finally defeat him. Then the prisoner would be thrown upon the sun disk for the removal of his heart. Sahagan, who collected careful records of Aztec ceremonies, has left a particularly harrowing account of those victims (probably the more imaginative) whose courage failed them:

> Some captives there were who lost consciousness when they found themselves bound to the stone; they threw themselves to earth without taking up any weapons, desiring that they be killed at once—and so they did, throwing them upon their backs on the edge of the stone.

It is recorded that one great warrior from Tlaxcala succeeded in exhausting all five Knights. He was released and sent to lead

Aztec armies. On returning victorious, however, he insisted on being sacrificed, apparently believing that as the Sun God had decreed that he should be taken prisoner he must accept his fate. And by dying on the stone he could win a place in the ranks of the soldiers, either killed in battle or sacrificed, whose privilege it was to escort the sun up the heavens to the zenith. (After noon it was accompanied to its setting by women who had died in childbirth—for they too 'had died taking a man prisoner'.)

While the blossoming war was waged on behalf of the Sun God by his chosen people, captives from this or from ordinary wars of conquest might be sacrificed to other gods in the pantheon. Indeed, while the Sun God seems to have received by far the greatest number of hearts (boxes were richly carved on purpose to contain them), some of the most horrifying rites were devoted to other deities. Women and children were regularly sacrificed to earth and corn goddesses and the rain gods; at one rain and fertility festival a girl and a boy were drowned in a canoe laden with human hearts. For Xipe-totec, God of Spring, the victims were flayed and the skins donned by officiating priests. Sahagan describes a rite in honour of both Xipe and Huitzilopochtli.

> At this feast they killed all the prisoners, men, women and children. The owners of the prisoners handed them over to the priests at the foot of the temple, and they pulled them by the hair up the steps; and if they did not wish to go they were dragged to the block of stone where they were to kill them, and taking from each one his heart, they hurled the bodies down the steps where other priests flayed them. After they had been flayed the old men took them to the Calpulco where the owner of the captive had made his offering . . . there they dismembered them and sent a limb to Montezuma to eat, and the rest they shared among the priests and relatives.

Still grimmer is his account of a feast of the ancient Fire God:

Each of the nobles took his captive by the hair ... and they brought those that were to be cast into the fire and sprinkled their faces with incense [this was in fact a stupefying drug—the one merciful touch] ... They took them and fastened their hands behind them and bound their feet. Then they threw them over their shoulders and carried them to the top of the temple where there was a great fire and a heap of coals. They gave them to the fire. And there in the fire the prisoner began to twist and retch ... and he being in such agony they brought him out with hooks, and placed him on the stone and opened his breast, took out the heart and threw it at the feet of the statue of Xiuhtecutli, god of fire.

As for numbers, one record says that at the dedication of an enlargement of the Great Temple at Tenochtitlan (it had twin shrines dedicated to Huitzilopochtli and the Rain God Tlaloc) 20,000 prisoners were sacrificed. A Conquistador claimed to have counted many thousands of skulls in the rack which stood in the plaza below. These numbers may have been exaggerated, but they seem to represent the approximate truth.

I have dwelt upon these horrors as a necessary introduction to the second approach to Aztec religion, the psychological. On the one hand they will probably make any honest reader admit to himself that however genuinely he is horrified by the descriptions, they also have a potent fascination. On the other, they reveal how far the Aztecs went into the darkness, what dreadful acts could be performed by priests chosen as 'humble, peace-loving ... compassionate, friends of all ... and devout'.

It requires a great effort to go behind the creeds and forms of religions to the minds of their creators and possessors. The temples and churches, the shrines, altars and idols, the vestments and headdresses, the prayers, incantations, litanies and hymns, the ritual and sacred dances have such a clear and confident existence in themselves, that it is hard indeed fully to realize that all have come into being through the imaginations of individuals and groups and are continuously modified and

159

developed by them. Within that great arc of cultural forms possible to mankind, the range of religious expression is so enormous as to be almost absurd. How can men conceive divinities of such contrary tempers, holding such contrary values, desiring such contrary forms of service? There are peoples who have developed religious ideas that allow them to be as light-hearted and guilt-free as many of the South Sea Islanders, or as grim and guilt-ridden as the Calvinists, who rejoice in simplicity like the Quakers or in grandeur like the Roman Catholics, Incas, Egyptians—and indeed most other ancient civilized peoples. Yet always, because of the slow-growing forms of tradition, we are inclined to think of the religion shaping the faithful instead of the faithful shaping the religion.

Narrowing the subject to that of sacrifice, the range of possibility is no less. It stretches from the Hindu belief that all animal life is so sacred that even a fly must be spared (though, indeed, a wife may sacrifice her own life) to the human slaughter of the Aztecs. There are also the two forms of sacrifice—of the god for men, of men for the god. The first, usually involving the symbolic eating of the dead god's body, represents lonely man's longing for reunion with the cosmos. The second, although it may develop more spiritual overtones, represents the simple human conviction that man must pay the gods for what he wants from them, and appease their wrath. Often there is an underlying idea that the offerer is sacrificing himself to his god, but in fact he gives instead his animals, his children, his slaves or captives. Both types of sacrifice may be found among the same people, as they were among the Aztecs.

What is of significance here is the fact that while most peoples develop a growing tenderness and reluctance to kill in the name of their divinities, a few others indulge in ever-mounting holocausts. In those societies which turn towards the light, first human sacrifice is abandoned, often by the substitution of models or purely symbolic enactments, then the offering of animals is left behind until it is realized, as it was by the

Egyptians of the Middle Kingdom, that 'more acceptable is the character of a man of just heart than the ox of the evildoer'.

The Aztecs went further than any other people on earth in the opposite direction. There is a tendency among the scientifically minded to refuse all judgment, to say that the whole society genuinely believed that the Sun God had to be fed with human life if he was not to fail, and that the victims died confident of a reward in the after-life.

While there is truth in this point of view, I can no longer fully accept it. For there is not only the mountain of pain and suffering involved, almost intolerable to contemplate, but also the element of hypocrisy in the loving and compassionate priests who roasted men and pulled them off the fire in time to excise their living hearts. I am sure that the Aztec priests got pleasure from their holocausts, knew the same fascination that I suggest will have come from reading descriptions of their doings, but magnified a thousandfold in the actual presence of terror, suffering, blood, blisters and death. It is the same pleasurable fascination felt by Hitler's minions and, as I shall claim, by some abnormal few of those who glorify H-bombs. Once a society allows this dark aspect of the psyche to wax and to come uppermost, then there will be plenty of individuals in whom these pleasurable lusts are stronger than they are in most of us, who will enjoy themselves as priests, superintendents of camps and their gas chambers, advocates of nuclear war. And they will not only carry on the evil tradition they have inherited but will add to it as they can.

It may help to discover why certain societies move in this direction if other associated characteristics can be recognized. They are usually, I think, repressive societies in which sexual love, emotional expression and personal freedom are sternly curbed. They are societies inclined to see everything in terms of black and white, sin and virtue—with themselves the Children of Light and all others Children of Darkness. A hard and fast morality follows from the black and white view of sin and virtue, and a severe discipline enforces the morality, penances and mortification failure to maintain it.

The Tenocha Aztecs came into the Valley later than most of the other invading tribes, and in their early days suffered defeat and crushing humiliation. Yet they were always aggressive, and established the myth that their Sun God was to lead them to victory over their neighbours, that he had commanded them to maintain the military discipline, the denial of the individual, of a dedicated warrior race. They therefore developed all the characteristics of a repressive society. Sin was for them synonymous with drunkenness and sexual liberty. In expiation or to please their gods they practised horrible penances of slashing themselves and drawing blood from ears and tongue with cactus spines. On many occasions they perforated their tongues and drew through them a cord threaded with these barbed spines. Even today the Flagellantes run through the streets of Mexico flogging and being flogged, their backs streaming with blood.

The Aztecs' image of themselves as a chosen people was even more dangerous than such images usually are, for it was charged with the hate and desire for revenge that follows from subjection and humiliation. So when success came to them and they fought their way to power and riches, they had become peculiarly charged with violence and dark urges, and hence, after the inevitable ways of the psyche, peculiarly inclined to see their supposed enemies as charged with violence and dark urges. As one of their own most sympathetic historians has written, in addition to believing they had to support the sun with human sacrifice they 'also believed they had an ethical ideal to attain. The struggle of the sun against the powers of darkness was not only a struggle of the gods, but it was also, above all, the struggle of good against evil. The mission of the Aztecs was, then, to be on the side of the sun, the symbol of good, opposing the fearful gods of darkness, the symbols of evil.' So the temple pyramids became a human shambles and the Aztecs perpetrated the most dreadful deeds ever celebrated in religion's name. Speaking from their conscious minds, the priests still proclaimed their virtue and loving-kindness, their glorious duty of maintaining the light of the world, but within them the dark side of the psyche that is in us all had grown, had corrupted and had taken possession. They enjoyed what they did, and Huitzilopochtli the sun of the day became in truth the sun of darkness.

It is not often that I make a mocking comparison between the religious beliefs and acts of the past and the physical facts as revealed by modern science. It would be so crudely brutal that even in a cynical mood one would feel it 'not fair' to our poor species. But it would also, evidently, be the height of folly, for who shall deny that any endeavour of mind and spirit and feeling towards something greater than animal survival, any heightening of consciousness, may contribute to the meaning of the vast processes in which our solar system is humbly involved? But in a religion as corrupt as the Aztec I am irresistibly tempted to do so. There, in the lofty valley of the great American Isthmus, the people labour to raise their priests two hundred feet nearer to the heavens. On the summits of these little pyramids the priests plunge their obsidian blades, and raise still pulsating hearts at arms' length towards the sun. If they did not do so the sun would die, the seasons stand still. Below their feet the earth turns on its axis and swings round the sun, fixed in

the vast procession of the days and seasons. Ninety-three million miles above their heads the sun burns, hydrogen turns into helium and the released energy floods out as it has done through 4,000,000,000 years and is likely to do for as many million to come.

AZTEC SACRIFICE TO THE SUN

SOL INVICTUS

THE LAST TWO chapters have shown how two peoples, living far removed in time and space yet at much the same stage of culture, developed their solar worship in opposite directions. Both were theocracies dependent on peasant cultivators, both built splendid sun temples and ceremonial cities, both felt themselves to be under the special patronage of the Sun God. In the Egypt of Akhenaten, however, he flooded his light upon a world of love, of humane and vital art, of delight in all earthly life, and cared little for fixed moralities, for sin, penance and punishment. In the Mexico of the Aztecs he came to be a voracious destroyer; his beams threw into harsh relief a grim art and a life-denying morality enforced by penance and sacrifice.

Now I have to follow the story of man's relationship with the sun into an altogether new phase. The first experience of Old World civilization when religion, blossoming spontaneously from the psyche, united societies in total dependence on their gods, was faltering and coming to an end. The change which began to take place during the last millennium B.C. centred on a growing self-awareness in the individual. Each step since man had left behind his wholly animal past had been marked by his further separation from the natural matrix. The light of the conscious intellect brightened and was focused more sharply on the individual predicament, on society, religion, and even upon nature itself. The old intuitive expression of unconscious forms came in for a keener scrutiny, and as a result men and women were more burdened by their souls, more deeply anxious for their private salvation.

Whether this was solely due to the inescapable lessons of time, the discovery that great god-centred empires could fall to pieces, civilizations collapse and even the economics of everyday life fail, leaving individuals utterly at a loss, or whether it was the more or less inevitable outcome of a cosmic evolution of consciousness, is for each of us to judge.

Certainly it was helped on by the invention of alphabetical writing. Ideas could now be recorded with much more ease and flexibility and by a greater number and variety of people, so that observations, questions and answers, inspired guesses, which before had too often flitted through the mind, been expressed in fleeting speech and soon been forgotten or allowed to become blurred, could now be fixed in permanent clarity and accumulated from generation to generation.

Before going on to describe the part which the Sun God played in the mystery religions which were the oriental response to the new age, and to the great flourish of solar monotheism in which paganism ended in the Roman Empire, I want to go back for a moment to the earlier history of the Indo-European peoples who are to play so considerable a part in the remainder of this chronicle. Perhaps I would not bother to do so, perhaps I would plunge directly ahead, were it not for one very solid thing: Stonehenge. The most massive monument in the Old World, the Pyramid of Cheops, and what many might judge to be the most impressive momument in the New World, the Sun Pyramid at Teotihuacan, were both raised in solar worship. It is a remarkable testimony to the creative power of the star that the greatest monument of prehistoric Europe was also a sanctuary of the Sun God.

Although the history of the expansion of the peoples speaking

Indo-European languages is still very imperfect, there is no doubt that they were radiating far and wide through Asia and Europe during the second millennium B.C. They were successful pastoralists, and almost everywhere they imposed themselves as a ruling class, drawing their wealth from flocks and herds. They moved in the atmosphere of an Heroic Age. Everywhere, too, as far as we can tell, they introduced religions in which the celestial gods were pre-eminent. If a paternal sky god, a Zeus, was at least nominally supreme, the Sun God was always at his elbow. In the Kuban, where warrior graves dating from about 2500 B.C. illustrate their original way of life perhaps as clearly as we shall ever see it, the chiefs were buried with the battle-axes that were their characteristic weapons, and with disks or kidney-shaped emblems in gold that were certainly a part of a solar cult.

The centre of dispersal of these battle-axe-using Indo-European peoples seems to have been the grasslands of Russia north of the Black Sea and the Caspian. From here they thrust eastward into Iran, and then over the passes into the Punjab, where they helped to bring the Indus Civilization to an end in about 1500 B.C. The early Aryan unity of the Iranians and these invaders of India is shown by the many similarities between the Rig Veda and the Persian Avesta.

The southward movement of the Indo-Europeans is best represented by the Mitanni who entered western Mesopotamia, the ruling class among the Hittites in Asia Minor and the Greek-speaking Mycenaeans who had established themselves in Greece by 1500 B.C. Later, as is well known, further Greek-speaking peoples, including the Achaeans and Dorians, followed in the wake of the Mycenaeans, while the Italians occupied their promontory, the Spaniards theirs. In the north the Teutonic tribes took shape, and powerful Celtic-speaking peoples emerged in South Germany, Switzerland and France, many groups of them crossing to the British Isles during the Late Bronze and Iron Ages there. But long before these later

Celts arrived to give Britain the name by which she is now
most commonly known, warrior groups armed with a type
of weapon found from the Atlantic to the Pontic region already
suggested as the centre of Indo-European dispersal, had fought
their way right across Europe and had formed an element in
invasions of Britain. These began as early as 1750 B.C., and the
ruling class of warrior pastoralists which they introduced survived to contribute much to the wealthy pastoral and trading
society which began to flourish in Wessex some two centuries
later.

In their expansion to the south and west, the Indo-European
peoples, with their devotion to celestial deities, again and again
encountered the peoples whose religious beliefs still, as it were,
looked downward towards the chthonic powers of the earth.
Cults of the Mother Goddess had been carried by the early
cultivators along the Mediterranean and into western Europe
and Britain. The clash between the divinities of the heavens and
of the earth took place with dramatic clarity, for example,
when the Greek-speaking peoples entered the Minoan world,
and it happened at a humbler level when the first warrior
peoples of the Early Bronze Age, with their wealth in cattle
and sheep, landed in a Britain then in the possession of a stone-
using peasantry. The religious encounter is embodied at Stonehenge. This place, now visited by thousands of people from all
over the world, was originally the site of a New Stone Age
sanctuary. At that time instead of standing stones pointing
towards the sky there were pits pointing down into the earth,
and the deities served there may be assumed to have been of the
underworld where they could be reached by the pouring of
libations. Then came the invasions by the pastoralists whom we
have recognized as in part at least Indo-European, and the holy
ground was taken over for a temple built with the famous Blue
Stones brought over two hundred miles from south-west
Wales. Already this second Stonehenge had its entrance facing
down the ceremonial Avenue towards the point on the horizon

where the sun rose at the midsummer solstice. Then as the new rulers gained in power and social organization they were able to command the labour and the skill to rebuild the temple on a far more magnificent scale. There was an outer lintelled ring of sandstone blocks and an inner horseshoe of trilithons, each consisting of two colossal upright stones supporting a lintel, which can perhaps be seen as portals opening on the heavens. The open end of this horseshoe, and of the little Blue Stone horseshoe which echoed it, were turned towards the Avenue and the midsummer sunrise, the furthest point towards the north attained by the rising sun.

The whole temple with its many openings upon the sky may well have been used for measuring the rising and setting of moon, planets, stars and constellations, but the orientation of the mighty trilithons must prove that here at Stonehenge, as elsewhere, the supreme deity was the Sun God himself.

In certain of the graves of chiefs living in Wessex at the time of the second, Blue Stone temple at Stonehenge, the dead had been provided with a disk of beaten gold bearing a bold equal-armed cross at the centre, giving the effect of a four-spoked wheel. There can be no reasonable doubt that these were sun symbols. Close by Stonehenge itself, and dating from the magnificent third phase of the temple, two richly furnished women's graves contained little ornaments which are among the most famous objects in British archaeology. They are amber disks mounted in wide gold rings, the rings themselves chased with many concentric circles. They are famous because a very similar ornament has been found at Knossos, proving trade contacts between Wessex and the eastern Mediterranean. Here they are of more significance because they, too, are very probably sun symbols. Although lacking the cross of the solar wheel, this identification seems plain enough. When fresh and polished the amber would have glowed a golden red, and when rubbed, perhaps on woollens woven from the downland sheep, it would grow warm and magnetic. Combined with gold, the metal of the sun, and the traditional disk shape with its concentric circles, the solar image is surely unmistakable?

It seems fairly sure, then, that among the men and women allowed to pass within the ring-bank marking the sacred precincts of Stonehenge many would have worn these badges of their solar cult, just as today Christians (and especially women) wear gold or jewelled crosses. If at the seasonal festivals they gathered in the holy of holies inside the trilithons to worship the sun at its rising or zenith, then its rays would have been reflected back from these glowing, winking replicas of its own divine face.

It is these disks rather than the unique temple itself which most clearly link the cult of the Sun God in Britain with that of the adjacent parts of the continent. Peoples among whom the battle-axe-wielding, horse-breeding pastoralists from the east were strongly represented appeared in north-western Europe at much the same time as their kinsmen first crossed into Britain. And in just the same way as in these islands they established themselves as an aristocracy among the agriculturists of the Stone Age. At the period when Stonehenge was brought to its most magnificent and for some centuries afterwards, their descendants left evidence to prove them ardent sun worshippers.

The most astonishing relic comes from a Danish bog at Trundholm in north-west Zealand (if only something like it could have been found at Stonehenge!). It is a bronze and gold sun chariot. Six four-spoked wheels support a framework carrying a large disk engraved on both sides with circles and spirals. One of its faces is still sheeted with gold, and it may be that originally both were gilded. In front stands a smooth and shapely, but surprisingly static, horse with a loop on its breast which probably held a rein running back to another loop on the edge of the disk. The whole device is quite large enough to have been drawn along in procession. The repetition of sun symbols on this most sacred object is very striking. As well as the golden disk itself there are the circles and spirals it bears, the six solar wheels and also star-like rays radiating from the horse's eyes.

The Bronze Age ladies of Denmark often carried on their belts circular bronze boxes that probably served them in lieu of handbags. The lids of these, which seem generally to have been worn just above the navel, were ornamented with circle and spiral patterns very much like those on the chariot disk. I think there is little doubt that they were deliberately engraved as solar patterns. If so, then they were the feminine counterpart to the bronze razors used by the men.

Some of these razors ended in a horse's head as a handle, and the horse, perhaps partly because it was much honoured among the Indo-European peoples and partly because it drew the sun chariot, was a solar beast. Others had a solar wheel for their handle. Again many of these razors were engraved on the blade with rayed circles and sometimes with a boat that might be carrying a sun disk amidships. This crowded iconography suggests that in Bronze Age Denmark shaving was a ritual act.

Across the Skagerrak in Norwegian Ostfold and Swedish Bohuslan the very same motifs recur in a totally different setting. In that part of the world the glaciers of the Ice Age have ground smooth and left exposed wide expanses of rock. Some are thickly covered with Bronze Age engravings. Boats are the commonest subjects. They lie there in their hundreds, almost identical with those on the Danish razors and, like them, sometimes carrying a solar disk and sometimes what has been called a kidney-shaped figure that may conceivably represent the setting or the rising sun. Though much less common, there are also engravings showing the horse-drawn solar chariot. So here on this northern coast is the iconography of the sun so well known from the earliest writings of the Indians and Greeks: the chariot with which Helios or Apollo drove by day across the sky, and the barque by which the Sun God was carried back to

VI. CARVED SUN WHEEL: Temple of Konarak, India

the east each night through the waters of the underworld. Not even the survival of their languages evokes more strongly the unity of tradition underlying the great, haphazard, untidy dispersal of the Indo-European peoples.

I have been tempted to follow these peoples into the barbaric mists of western and northern Europe chiefly by the attraction of that potent physical manifestation of the Sun God: Stonehenge. Yet the excursion has its value in helping to interpret the beliefs of the Indo-Europeans whose migrations carried them in the opposite direction, into the Asiatic lands where high civilizations had flourished before them. For the evidence from Britain and Scandinavia, and at least equally from the early sun-worshipping chiefs of the Kuban, reveals that in their more primitive state the skyward worship of the Indo-Europeans tended to concentrate upon the greatest of the heavenly bodies, and result yet again in the supremacy of the Sun God.

In India and Persia where the rich inheritance from the past civilized the pastoral nomads far more rapidly, and where therefore more subtle priestly theology was bound to diverge from the beliefs and practices of the simple people, the supreme celestial divinity came to be seen as a god of spiritual and moral light. Nevertheless the simpler concept had certainly been there in the beginning and was daily renewed alike for peasant and poet by the glory and life-giving power of the star itself.

India possessed the shadowy and neglected high god, so often encountered in this chronicle, in Dyaus Pitar. He represents the Indo-European sky father at his most generalized, the fading counterpart of Zeus Pater and Jupiter. His faint solar aspect appears in the Rig Veda where he 'smiles through the clouds', yet already he is vague, he has no hymns devoted to him alone —he, too, has been kicked upstairs.

His power was drawn out of him by other heavenly deities, by Indra, the god of storm who became the conquering pastoralists' war god, and in his aspect as a god of light by the twin brothers Mitra and Varuna. Mitra was certainly a solar divinity, but he was dominated by his twin, whose Sanskrit name means 'sky', and the two together were sometimes recognized as two aspects of Eternal Light. In the Rig Veda Varuna is very powerful; alone or together with Mitra he is hailed as king of both gods and men, and he has many other royal and sovereign titles. He and his brother drive a chariot across the heavens with rays as arms; their beautiful hands may recall in significance those of the Aten. They dwell in a celestial palace of gold with a thousand columns and a thousand doors. While Varuna is sometimes shown as sitting in this palace and receiving information brought to him by the sun, and as controlling the movements of all the heavenly bodies and the seasons, he is also immanent in these things. Thus he wears a golden cloak and shining robes, characteristic dress for the Sun God, while again and again the eye of Mitra and Varuna is proclaimed to be the sun. Indeed, Varuna acquired very much of the 'all-seeing eye' attribute of the Sun God. From being far-sighted and thousand-eyed he becomes 'the lord of holy order, the watcher of men, whose vigilance nothing can escape'. In short at his height he was the supreme controller, ordering both the moral and the physical world. Curiously enough in later literature Varuna lost his power as king of physical and moral light. While Mitra was still identified with the sun and daylight, Varuna was assigned the moon and night. Finally he seems to have become a minor divinity controlling rain and the oceans.

The simplest embodiment of the Sun God in India was Surya, the sun itself. He shone for the world, for gods and men, and drove away the powers of darkness, witches, disease and evil dreams. He was the husband of Ushas, the Dawn, and drove a chariot, sometimes with one horse, sometimes with seven or more. He seems to be one of the Sun Gods, now familiar, who have far more power and worship than their place in the pantheon would suggest. In the Bhavishya Purana it is said 'Because there is none greater than he [Surya], nor has been, nor will be, therefore he is celebrated as the supreme soul in all the Vedas.' And in the Brahma Purana the sun is addressed under twelve names, including all the greatest of the pantheon, as though all were but aspects of the Sun God. His worship continues, for at dawn the devout Brahman addresses to him the Gayatri, most sacred text of the Vedas:

> Let us meditate on that excellent glory of the divine Vivifier
> May he enlighten our understanding.

The ease with which Surya was related with Varuna, and something of the spirit of Indian sun worship, are expressed in this portion of one of the Vedic hymns addressed to him:

> *Light-giving Varuna, thy piercing glance does scan*
> *In quick succession all this stirring, active world,*
> *Measuring our days and night, and spying out all creatures.*
> *Surya with flaming locks, clear-sighted god of day,*
> *Thy seven ruddy mares bear on thy rushing car.*
> *. . . To thy refulgent orb.*
> *Beyond this lower gloom, and upward to the light*
> *Would we ascend, O Sun! Thou god among the gods.*

I could say much more about sun worship in India—about the Asvins, mysterious deities of light, the divine order Rta imposed by Varuna which has so much in common with the Egyptian Ma'at, about Agni the Fire God who may have been messenger between gods and men because he so plainly represented the solar fire on earth, and about Savitr, counterpart of Surya, an all-gold god—with yellow hair, and eyes, hands, arms and tongue of gold—who may perhaps have been the sun as a source of energy in man. But India was too far away and cut off to contribute substantially to the religious developments in the classical world which are the main subject of this chapter. It has been enough to show how there at the eastern extremity of their dispersal the Indo-European peoples had carried some of the same religious ideas which inspired the worshippers at Stonehenge, the men who drew the Trundholm sun chariot in

173

procession and those who carved the rocks along the shores of
the Skagerrak.

I want now to return across the mountain barrier to Persia,
for there lay not only the oriental source of the mystery religion
of greatest significance in this history, but also a native religion
which demonstrates with perfect clarity the change in consciousness described at the beginning of this chapter.

The single origin revealed in the language, forms and religious feeling of the Rig Veda and the Iranian Avesta has
already been mentioned, and the fact that many of the gods
common to both represent something at least of the ancient
Indo-European pantheon has been confirmed by their appearance in Mitannian inscriptions. Yet the Avesta has been in some
ways very deeply altered by the individual teaching of Zarathushtra, the much mythologized yet essentially historical
prophet of Zoroastrianism. Although it is uncertain exactly
when he lived, it was before the middle of the last millennium
B.C., and he may therefore be hailed together with the Hebrew
prophets as the first of the great psychological and religious
innovators. In fact he was the herald of the extraordinary
spiritual and intellectual flowering of the sixth century,
when Lao Tse, Confucius, the Buddha, Pythagoras, Heraclitus
and other leading Greek scientists were all living at one
time.

In Persia Varuna became Ahura Mazda. He, too, presided
over a divine physical and moral order, and he, too, was closely
linked with Mithra, who even more clearly than his Indian
counterpart was a solar divinity. While probably the pre-
Avesta Ahura Mazda was a general sky god, representing the
light of heaven, the ultimate Indo-European celestial All Father
in Persia as in India was Dyaus Pitar. The tendency for sky gods
to concentrate into what men saw every day as the greatest of
celestial powers and become Sun Gods is by now already
familiar. I do not see how this solar aspect can be withheld from
the original Ahura Mazda. Was not his symbol the winged

solar disk? In that most famous of all Persian inscriptions, the colossal Darius bas-relief carved on the cliff-face at Behistun, Darius the Great, standing head and shoulders above his followers, is shown raising his right arm in salutation to the god who hovers in the air above him in the form of the winged disk. The text, recording in three languages Darius's overthrow of his rivals for the throne, concludes with the words 'Darius proclaims: Ahura Mazda came to my aid.' I see no reason to doubt that the winged disk which stood for Horus in Egypt, for Assur in Assyria, also stood for a divinity with a powerful solar aspect in Persia. Those who deny this because Ahura Mazda was also said to transcend the sun, to control it and appear before it at the dawn, simply do not know their Sun God. Evidently the makers of electric bulbs agree with me, for is not the round shining Mazda bulb unmistakably our indoor sun?

However I do not want to linger over the proof that in early, pre-Avesta, Persia, Ahura Mazda was in part an Indo-European solar divinity. For what is of significance at this stage of the history of the Sun God is the change in his nature brought about by Zarathushtra. As the individual self-consciousness increased and the conscious and intellectual mind grew further apart from the unconscious, there was an equivalent tendency to set a single male divinity outside and above nature, the world being his creation, sometimes his creation as Logos, the most intellectual of conceptions. It is not easy to distinguish sharply between transcendental and immanent gods, for there is always something in man that wishes to draw the transcendent back into nature. Did not the ageing Wordsworth work over his poems trying to conceal the intuitive pantheism of his early inspiration? Perhaps the Hebrews made Jahveh more consistently transcendental than any of his contemporaries, yet even he seems sometimes to creep back into his works.

Zarathushtra took Ahura Mazda and made him sole creator of the universe. He was all-powerful, all-wise and all-good.

Immediately the prophet was up against the insoluble difficulty which has beset all transcendental monotheisms and besets them still: the need to explain why such a deity created and countenances evil. Zarathushtra's solution, as expressed in the Gathas, the most ancient part of the Avesta generally attributed to the prophet himself, was to say that Ahura Mazda who had created both light and darkness, good and evil, had created the twin spirits Spenta Mainyu (Good Mind) and Angra Mainyu (Evil Spirit), who, as a concession to more primitive ideas, were allowed attendant hosts of angels of light and demons of darkness. These two spirits did not exist independently but in opposition to each other, and both met in the higher being of Ahura Mazda. It was the duty of man on earth to fight for the powers of good against evil; the good would triumph in the end, yet the efforts of each man contributed to its victory. For 'the central idea of Zarathushtra's religion is the individuality of Man and his responsibility towards the Universe. Before him the individual person and his life counted for little . . . in recognizing the individual as a free agent on whose decision the fate of the world depended, Zarathushtra boldly broke with the religious views of his time. Everybody has to decide for himself whether to align himself with the Good or side with the Evil.' Thus in the teaching of this prophet, a true product of the new age of heightened individual consciousness, the old Sun God of nature had almost entirely given way to the new one of moral light. Yet the simpler ideas lingered on, doubtless more strongly in those who were inarticulate than in those whose words have been recorded. For instance the Indo-European idea of the god in his chariot lives in a hymn to the sun from the Avesta. It begins:

> We sacrifice to the undying, shining, swift-horsed Sun. When the light of the sun waxes warmer, when the brightness of the sun waxes warmer, then up stand the heavenly Yazatas by hundreds of thousands. They gather together its glory, they make its glory pass down, they pour its glory upon the earth made by

Ahura, for the increase of the world of holiness, for the increase of the creatures of holiness, for the increase of the undying, shining, swift-horsed Sun.

Then after proclaiming the purifying powers of the sun and the danger that would come from the demons should it fail to rise, it goes on:

He who offers up sacrifice unto the undying, shining, swift-horsed Sun—to withstand darkness, to withstand the Daevas born of darkness, to withstand the robbers and bandits . . . to withstand death that creeps in unseen—offers it up to Ahura Mazda, offers it up to Amesha-Spentas, offers it up to his own soul.

Indeed the image of the chariot persisted in most tangible form. The Persian army of Xerxes was followed by a chariot of the Sky God drawn by eight white horses, and in writing of Cyrus, Xenophon says that this might be followed by another belonging to the Sun God. Here was the distant but true relative of the small bronze trundler from the Zealand bog.

Another manifestation of the solar element in Zoroastrianism is preserved in the religion of the Parsees, Persian refugees from the Arab conquest who have lived in India ever since. It seems that fire, that ancient solar symbol, was always the symbol of Ahura Mazda, and among the Parsees it still plays a great part. Their places of worship are 'fire-temples' where the sacred fire burns perpetually on the altar. There is a fire sanctuary, too, near each Tower of Silence, where the dead are exposed to be devoured by vultures. The Parsees keep close to the Good Life of Zarathushtra, being known throughout the world for their benevolence and honesty. Yet they prosper and grow rich, have attained a life in the sun. In this they are the Indian counterpart of our Quakers—and it may be remembered that the Quakers, too, depend upon the image of the Inner Light.

Zarathushtra himself seems largely to have avoided a dualism of equal powers of good and evil by the device of the two

spirits, yet there is a hint even in the early Avesta that Angra
Mainyu was an aspect of a greater power of darkness, equal and
eternal enemy to Ahura. This, certainly, was the direction in
which Iranian religion was to develop. Ahriman, the Lie,
became coeval with Ahura Mazda, and under the priesthood
of the Magi this emerged into a total dualism. For them Ormazd
(compounded of Ahura and Spenta Mainyu) was in everlasting
opposition to Ahriman. As two equal principles of good and
evil they were expressed as Good and Evil, Light and Darkness, celestial Heaven and black, cavernous Hell.

Although after the lofty moral teaching of Zarathushtra
himself his religion became considerably debased, and under
the Magi full of magic and superstition, it nevertheless remained
a strong, and in general virtue-inducing creed (the Parsees
remain as proof) and became the official religion of Persia as
late as Sassanian times. During this long history Iranian dualism,
expressed in the terms of light and darkness which find so ready
a response in the creatures of our turning globe, had a marked
influence on Judaeo-Christian apocalyptic literature. In particular Satan, Prince of Darkness, and his followers can hardly be
distinguished from Ahriman and his demon host. This influence
has been made all the plainer by discoveries among the Dead
Sea Scrolls. In the *Manual of Discipline* it is told how the God of
Israel shaped two spirits; 'they are the spirits of truth and error.
In the abode of light are the origins of truth, and from the
source of darkness are the origins of error. In the hand of the
prince of light is dominion over all the sons of righteousness . . .
and in the hand of the angel of darkness is all dominion over the
sons of error . . .' These ideas, then, were powerful among the
Essenes and they shine out clearly from the gospel of St. John.
"All that came to be was alive with his life [God as Logos], and
that life was the light of men. The light shines on in the dark,
and the darkness has never quenched it. There appeared a man
named John, sent from God; he came as a witness to testify to
the light . . . he was not himself the light; he came to bear

witness to the light. The real light [Jesus] which enlightens every man was even then coming into the world." So when, soon, I have to plunge into the bewildering religious maelstrom of the Graeco-Roman world, it must be remembered that images remotely descended from the Indo-European sun-worshippers had permeated Judaism already in Palestine.

But the more direct and important contribution which Iran was to make to the Graeco-Roman world was the mystery cult of Mithraism. In the common Aryan pantheon of the Iranians and Indians before their separation this celestial divinity had a high place—and his antiquity is confirmed by his name appearing in the Mitannian inscriptions of the mid-second millennium B.C. Just as Mitra was linked with Varuna in the Rig Veda, so was Mithra with Ahura Mazda in the Avesta. Indeed, in the days before Zarathushtra his name came first in the divine names as Mithra-Ahura. In the exalted teaching of the prophet himself he could find no place, but he survived in the minds of those who preferred their deity to shine in the sky rather than in the new-fangled moral conscience, and came in the end to be the centre of a mystery cult in which morality and mysticism were equally blended.

In what seem to be fragments of pre-Zarathushtra songs incorporated in the Avesta are two pieces addressed to Mithra in peace and in war. They contain several mentions of the god's car: 'At his chariot pull four horses, white, of one colour, feeding heavenly fodder, immortal.' Here is the origin of the white-horsed chariots that went with the Persian hosts.

Another ancient fragment says of Mithra:

> *For whom the white racers*
> *Pull the harnessed chariot,*
> *The one wheel is of gold,*
> *And the jewels hold all-light.*

These lines introduce one of the most fascinating of the minor attributes of the Indo-European Sun God—or rather they reintroduce it, for it has already begun to appear among the sun-worshippers of western and northern Europe. This is the solar wheel, one of the most irresistible and infectious symbols in the solar iconography. The 'one wheel' of Mithra's chariot is not for traction, but is the flaming wheel or nimbus nearly always shown behind the god of celestial light—behind Mitra-Varuna and Mithra-Ahura as he drives in his chariot. The jewels are the diamonds or rubies with which this great nimbus was evidently sometimes set and which were believed, like the sun, to hold their own light because they appeared to shine in the darkness.

The Persian kings ruled by divine grace, and as a sign of it were granted the *Hvareno*, a fiery aureole. This, it was recognized, was a celestial gift from the Sun God.

In the vision of the Book of Daniel, the Ancient of Days, the ultimate Creator, is seen enthroned. 'His throne was like fiery flame and his wheels as burning fire . . . and his countenance was as the sun when it shines in its strength.' There seems no doubt that the Ancient's wheels belonged to him and were his flaming nimbus and not, as many translations have it, wheels of the throne (an unknown image). Again in Ezekiel each Cherub has a fiery wheel behind him, also set with eye-stones or jewels. Although some part of this tradition of the halo or nimbus comes from Assyria, where the Sun God Assur is shown in the midst of one, and before them from Babylonia where a king of the first dynasty of Babylon brought into the sun temple (E-babbara) 'great sun disks of agate', the solar wheel from the Indo-European sun chariot must have coalesced with it. I need not insist how readily it passed into Christianity. How many thousands of hours must have been devoted by monks to drawing the disk with the equal-armed cross behind the head of Christ, the disciples and saints, and lovingly spreading them with gold? The haloes were often identical in every detail with those little gold disks buried with the Bronze Age ladies on Salisbury Plain.

In Christian iconography Christ passes from the cross of suffering to the cross of glory, the latter being shown with tremendous sun rays radiating from the centre. One of the greatest of these, a huge golden sunburst, shines on the high altar of St. Peter's in Rome. Again in the Catholic church the monstrance in which the Host is placed for adoration on the high altar is made in the likeness of a radiant sun.

To return at last to Mithra standing in his chariot before his jewelled golden wheel, he must certainly be recognized as a god of celestial light. He is often evoked together with sun, moon and stars; he could arrive ahead of the dawn and linger after the sun had set; the sun was sometimes called his eye. There was, moreover, a humbler sun deity called Haverseta. Yet we are now familiar enough with solar theology to know that in spite of all this, for many of his worshippers Mithra could also appear quite simply as the Sun God—and I think that his subsequent history makes it evident that he did so. This is supported by the fact that in Iran he was also the god of social law and order, suggesting that he did not lack that common attribute of the Sun God—his all-seeing eye.

Very little is known of the evolution of Mithra worship into the esoteric and sacramental cult of Mithraism. It is said that the evolution had already gone far by the fourth century B.C. when Alexander destroyed the Persian Empire. Their defeat brought the Persians more even than the usual bewilderment of a conquered people. Why had Ahura Mazda not come to their aid after their long worship, their long fight on his behalf against the Prince of Darkness? Why had Alexander, who seemed to them Ahriman incarnate, been granted the victory? With the tenacious religious faith of our species, instead of doubting their god, they blamed themselves. They must have failed in their observances. So many turned to a more rigid formalism of creed and rite. But it seems likely that others, already caught up in the new age and eager for personal salvation, found relief from their national tribulation in dedicating their lives to a cult.

The central 'mystery', the revelation accessible only to initiates, the progress up the series of initiatory orders, the rich and secret sacraments, would all bring relief to individuals in this plight. Nothing better expresses the new desire for the secret, the hidden, for personal regeneration, than the small underground temples of the Mithras cult. The god who had been worshipped in the light of his own rays in the great courts by the Nile, on the summit of pyramids in the Valley of Mexico, within the great rings of Stonehenge, was now carried down into a sunken room. Here only the altarpiece was brilliantly lit. It is a good expression of men's growing need to bring their heightened consciousness to terms with their unconscious minds.

So Mithraism took shape in Persia and then began its spread to the south and west. Babylon became an important centre, and there the cult made some small borrowings from the powerful astrology of the Chaldeans, at that time influencing the whole of the ancient world. The people of the Two Rivers had no difficulty in identifying Mithras with their ancient Sun God, Shamash. In Asia Minor, too, where the cult flourished and had a centre at Trebizond, the Greeks identified him with Helios. It was here, in all probability, that the young Mithras acquired the pointed cap in which he is nearly always depicted. For it seems to have been Greek artists of the school of Pergamum who first provided the cult with its artistic imagery—with the famous bull sacrifice scene that was to appear at every Mithraic altar, with the torch-bearers representing the morning, noon and midday sun and many other figures.

Mithraism did not enter the Roman world until the first century B.C., and then was not immediately successful. But after a century or two of obscurity as one among a motley crowd of oriental 'Mysteries' its popularity suddenly kindled among the soldiery, and the cult went with the legions as far as the shores of the Atlantic and the North Sea. It was also attractive to emperors seeking to strengthen the imperial dignity, for it still carried with it ideas of divine kingship and of the royal *Hvareno*, the fiery aureole granted by the Sun God.

If there had been doubt concerning the solar nature of Mithras in his Persian days, there could be none now. The Babylonians had recognized him as Shamash, the Greeks as Helios and Apollo: for the Romans he was none other than *Sol Invictus*, the Unconquerable Sun.

The myth of Mithras as it had now taken shape combined its own central story with details familiar from other mythologies. The beautiful youth was created from a rock by the power of Ormazd, this marvel being witnessed only by certain shepherds who thereupon brought gifts and adored him. He then clad himself in fig leaves and set about conquering such beings as had already been brought into existence. The first of these was the Sun, with whom he afterwards made a special bond of friendship. Ormazd then created a bull and Mithras did battle with it, being carried along on its horns before finally subduing it and dragging it into a cave. When the bull escaped and he overtook it once more, the Sun's servant, a raven, brought word that he must sacrifice the great beast. This he did, with a reluctance always poignantly expressed on his face in the sculptures, and from the blood of the sacrifice sprang all the life of the earth, including the first man and woman. Angered by all this success among the powers of light, Ahriman strove to destroy the newly created life. Mithras bravely defended his creation. From a deluge sent by Ahriman one man and his cattle (and presumably his wife?) escaped in an ark. A drought was ended by the god striking a rock with his arrow, causing water to gush out. Having defeated the Prince of Darkness, Mithras' mission on earth was at an end. He partook of a final meal, a love feast, with the Sun God before being carried up to heaven in a fiery chariot. He had been the creator and saviour of earthly life, and now he continued to protect his followers, to serve as mediator and conduct their souls up to the celestial realms. Some said that he would end the world with a fearful conflagration when only the faithful would be saved.

Members of the cult formed spiritual fraternities that were also social communities comparable to our nonconformist chapel groups. Probably in the early days most congregations were of humble origin (the Romans are said first to have learnt of Mithraism from Cilician pirates) and they remained absolutely democratic, dignity being determined by a man's degree within the cult and not by his worldly position. There were in all seven grades—numbered no doubt to correspond with the celestial Seven of Sun, Moon and the Five Planets that were so much a part of the background of thought of the age. The lowest was that of the Raven, servant of the Sun, then the Occult, and next the Soldier, standing for the struggle of light against darkness. Up to this degree the faithful were known as Servants, and it was only on attaining the fourth step of the Lion, symbol of the Sun as fire, that they were accepted as full initiates. The fifth grade was that of *Perses*, the Persian, the sixth of *Heliodromus*, courier of the Sun, and the last that of *Pater*, an apex of mystical initiation presumably reached by very few. These *Paters* were the supreme administrators, and probably included members of the professional priesthood.

Initiation from grade to grade was accompanied by rites that might try courage and endurance and were sometimes barbarous—though perhaps the less seemly survivals from the past such as being thrown over a pit of water with the hands bound in chicken entrails would have been dropped by the decorous patrician communities of Rome. The faithful accepted an austere moral code and the strength and courage manifest in Mithras himself were the most admired virtues. In this, and in the exclusion of women, lay the special appeal to the military. Yet at the same time purifying baptisms, communion meals of bread and water or wine to celebrate the last feast of Mithras and the Sun on earth, and the esoteric lore which must have been imparted with each advance in initiation, added their mystical appeal. With morality, courage, equal brotherhood, participation in the mystery and assurance of a celestial after-life for the virtuous—to say nothing of imperial sympathy—Mithraism was indeed an attractive faith. Three hundred years after the death of Christ it looked as though *Sol Invictus* would prove his name. Then, almost abruptly, the tables were turned and it was Christ who had conquered the Roman Empire and secured the future faith of the western world. The two religions had become bitterly opposed—for by that time they had so much in common.

MITHRAS
From a Roman carving

SUN OF SALVATION

I HAVE FOLLOWED MITHRAS worship so far into the heart of Rome and its history because it was one of the most powerful solar faiths there has ever been and because, in spite of all later accretions, it was directly descended from the sun worship of the ancient Indo-European peoples. But now I have to stand back to try to get a wider prospect of that abounding, chaotic Graeco-Roman world which was still scattered with ruins from Bronze Age civilization and yet noisy with the building of the future. For in the religious mêlée, the Sun God assumed other, and sometimes greater, guises in addition to that of Mithras, and illumined the mind with different kinds of light—natural, mystical, moral and scientific.

First it must be recalled that the Greeks and Romans were themselves originally of Indo-European stock and had brought into their Mediterranean peninsulas their versions of the ancient worship of divinities of the sky. As it happened, Zeus Pater and Jupiter retained far more power and service among them than Dyaus Pitar among the Indians and Iranians, and for that reason the Sun God had greater difficulty in asserting his supremacy. On the other hand the Sky Father himself could be identified with the sun. At Baalbek, for example, a splendid Roman temple was built during the second century A.D., and dedicated to Jupiter-Baal as the Sun, the city itself being known as

Heliopolis. (This is another of the great sun temples of the world.)

Not everyone agrees that Apollo was originally a god of light and the sun in the early days of the Olympians. Yet when he was born on the little island of Delos the foundations of the isle turned to gold, and so too did the olive trees and the river Inopus, while all day a round pool on the island shone with a golden light. Moreover a cock, herald of sunrise, was present at the birth of this strong and beautiful son of Zeus.

Again it is difficult not to understand his slaying of the great female dragon, the Delphine (or in later form the Python), as meaning the victory of the conscious over the unconscious mind. The deed was accomplished with the bow that the infant Apollo seized up the instant after his birth—and arrows are often interchangeable with sunbeams.

Even Apollo's genius for music and his love for the lyre were sometimes given a solar interpretation. There are descriptions of him playing while other gods and goddesses danced 'Beautiful and tall . . . alight with radiance. Brightly shone his feet and his raiment.' A Greek poet cried 'He brings all Nature into harmony . . . and the plectrum of his lyre is the bright ray of the sun.'

Even if in the Homeric age Apollo was not a god of celestial light and the sun, with a relationship with the Sun God Helios akin to that of Mithra for Haverseta, Huitzilopochtli with Tonatiuh, the Spirit with the Sun in Valencio's faith, this is what he soon became. From the fifth century B.C. onwards, Phoebus-Apollo converged more nearly with Helios. He drove the sun chariot, was freely identified with foreign Sun Gods such as Mithra, and finally played his part in the solar monotheism in which the Olympians ended. His importance in Rome undoubtedly soared when Augustus, first occupant of the imperial throne, claimed him as his special patron. Indeed, with a deep understanding of the old bond between crown and sun, Augustus even on occasion claimed to be a son of the Sun

God—like many a Pharaoh before him and Inca after him. I cannot leave Apollo without adding that it is fortunate for the pattern of this book that he was also the patron of Socrates and of the Ionian Greeks.

Helios himself was a straightforward Indo-European Sun God. Greek vase paintings in which he is seen driving his four-horsed chariot across the heavens (in one of them stars are shown as tumbling boys) are the most beautiful portrayals of this subject ever made. Apart from his identification with Apollo, he was not of lofty Olympian rank. Yet as the deity of the island of Rhodes he was honoured with the gigantic statue by Chares, the Colossus of Rhodes, which became one of the Seven Wonders of the World. So once more, even in a land where he was not supreme, the Sun God was able to inspire men to extraordinary creative achievement.

This, then, was one element in the mental life of the Graeco-Roman world: the religion of the official pantheon, a pantheon descended from the gods of the Indo-European pastoralists mingled with those of many Mediterranean and local deities and civilized, almost secularized, by Greek thought and Roman cosmopolitan life. It was the equivalent of the Church of England as an established institution of the state, with the prestige of ancient buildings, episcopal dignity, royal weddings, coronations and roots deep in the national tradition. For centuries these gods had dwelt and been worshipped in the greatest, most dominating temples of Rome and Athens; to worship them was respectable and to the religious-minded could still be inspiring; the myths and legends concerning them were learnt by every child and therefore patterned the mind of every adult. Above all in imperial times they stood round the throne supporting an emperor who after his death would himself be officially deified. Because of the temper of Greek thought they remained pleasantly amoral, not in the least inclined to divide into armies of light and darkness, divinities well fitted to preside in the background of the Good Life of the pagan ideal.

The heightening of individual self-awareness and detachment of the intellectual and conscious mind from its darker roots which spread across the Old World before the middle of the last pre-Christian millennium, surely found its purest and highest expression in Greece. It fired the Greek colonists in Ionia to a spirit of scientific detachment that enabled them to look at nature with secular eyes. Thus they were the first to see the sun not as a god (though this did not prevent them from simultaneously worshipping Apollo) but as a physical object the movement, size and shape of which could be measured and calculated. Pythagoras brightened the pure intellectual light of mathematical theory, while Socrates made his followers question all the old instinctive forms, those inherited from the Bronze Age past and those arising from the individual psyche. No wonder that the priests cried too much light, and the hemlock brought darkness.

In the Roman imperial age the light of reason, of balance, sanity and enquiry which had shone for the first time on earth from the Hellenic mind had become somewhat confused and dim, yet it was still all-pervading. All educated men were permeated by Greek thought, whatever the way they chose to use or distort it. If there was one unifying idea derived from the mingled philosophies and sciences of the time, it was that the whole universe of life and thought and matter was one, that it was founded on reason, that the cosmos was god and god the cosmos, and that man with his divine spark repeated this unity in microcosm.

Stoicism, the most influential of the philosophies, had been reshaped by failure and disillusion. The pride of Hellenism had fallen, the ideal of the city state lay discredited. The individual had to survive as he could in a chaotic society. And although the Romans, as opposed to the Greeks, were wealthy and successful imperialists they, too (like the Americans today), shared in this sense of disintegration. They, too, felt something had gone wrong and looked desperately round for answers or for inner salvation. One result of all this loss of faith and direction, and one which was an important element in Graeco-Roman life, was an overwhelming belief in Fortune, and, illogically linked with the Fortune, in Fate. Pliny said: 'We are so much at the mercy of chance, that Chance is our god.' So indeed she was, statues of the lady were everywhere, the Emperor had his own Fortuna just as Napoleon was to have his luck. It was a question of mood or temperament whether one preferred incalculable Fortune or inevitable Fate.

Now I have to introduce yet another ingredient into this confused intellectual and religious scene. This was astralism. It was an alien creed, derived from Babylonia and Syria (astrologers, whatever their origin, were known as Chaldeans), and yet it seems to have had a unifying influence on the late classical world. It certainly had much to do with the solar monotheism, the renewed worship of the Sun God in which classical paganism flared and died.

Astralism was, of course, directly descended from the ideas prevailing in ancient Mesopotamia and already encountered in this pursuit of the Sun God. The ideas which led to the belief that life on earth was the counterpart of celestial life, that the ordering of a kingdom should correspond with the order of the stars. By now it had become more formalized in its sacerdotalism, and had adapted itself to the heightened self-consciousness and importance of the individual. Every man and woman now had his personal relationship to the celestial Seven and the whole starry universe, every soul was a spark from the celestial light from which it descended and to which it returned. At the siege of Jerusalem Titus assured his soldiers that the souls of those who were killed would rise into the ether and be seated in the stars. Astrology had been deeply affected, too, by Greek science. Indeed, no one would have distinguished between astrology and astronomy. Since Aristotle it had been accepted that the divine order and harmony of heaven and earth depended on transparent spheres (often said to number eight) revolving about the earth, and this cosmology had become an essential part of astralism as it was also of many of the Mysteries.

Most of all it affected men's vision of what happened to the soul after death. Nearly all were now beginning to look up-ward, abandoning the older, humbler belief in a gloomy or shadowy underworld of twittering ghosts in favour of celestial bliss. The idea of ascension was widely accepted, but its nature and precise direction varied astonishingly. The more philo-sophic thought of the individual soul reuniting with the uni-versal; some had a vague, mellifluous picture of the poised soul eternally raptured by the music of the revolving spheres; according to their faith, others believed it went to dwell in the sun or the moon or soared as far as the eighth sphere of the fixed stars. Yet others again, more Platonic and transcendental in their views, saw the soul rising even beyond the eighth sphere, to a region of ineffable light and truth, to be in the presence of a godhead outside the physical universe. This, as will appear, became the belief of the most exalted of the devotees of a single and supreme Sun God.

Almost everyone, except Gnostics, Christians, Jews and a few incorrigible sceptics, believed the Sun, Moon, Planets and fixed stars to be 'gods visible and created', the 'heavenly race of gods'. This conviction enabled even the most philosophic to participate in a contemplation of the moon and stars by night and the sun by day which provoked powerful mystical emo-tion. It brought them both exaltation and, as they felt, moral purification. With it went a curious belief, bound up with the more general belief that man shared in the nature and stuff of the cosmos, that light could be contemplated only with light, that the human eye had close affinity with the heavenly orbs. Starlike eyes could contemplate the stars, sunlike eyes the sun. For centuries then, and throughout the classical world, men of the most diverse nature spent hours watching and communing with the sun, moon and stars.

One can imagine them in gardens, olive groves and atria, on

roof-tops and mountain-tops, in the great temple precincts of the Acropolis or the Palatine Hill. And this brings me back to a notion implicit in much of what I have written. That worship of the Sun God and all the heavenly bodies was constantly recharged by their actual physical presence and the impact they made upon man. Even today when we are so much confined by walls and roofs, dazzled by our puny but nearer lights, we all experience the extraordinary lift to the spirits brought by sunshine and moonlight, the expansion of the self that may come with a spring morning or a starry night. Thus there has always been a strange give and take. Religious rites have become more ornate, further removed from nature, worship of the sun has become worship of spiritual light, yet all this has been constantly renewed by that gaseous ball and its streaming light and heat. It is as though whatever the priest may be teaching, the body and the enmeshed psyche remember that the sun drew up life on earth and by its energy still maintains it.

There it was, then, a mental life as confused, contradictory, cosmopolitan and obviously transitional as our own. All the old strong, organic cultures had largely broken down and the great cities of the Roman Empire, particularly the centres of thought in North Africa, Greece and Italy itself, were full of men whose ideas and beliefs were as many-complexioned as their faces. The background of thought was provided by Greek science and philosophy even while the social attitude became dominated by the acceptance of Chance and Fate. Large in the background of the more purely religious scene was the rich, well-equipped official faith of the Graeco-Roman pantheon and the deified Caesars which, together with a proper pride in its Law, Army and Imperial Administration, made the backbone of life for the Roman Establishment. But more alive, and in many ways more progressive because they were the response to the new needs of the individual consciousness, its loneliness and its desire for communion, were the many sacramental Mystery religions, most of them oriental in spirit and devoted

192

to foreign gods. For Mithraism was only one among many such. There were those of Cybele and Attis, of the Egyptian Lord Serapis and Queen Isis, the Syrian Baal and Adonis, Dionysus and many more—some local, some oecumenical. Then there were the Orphic and Pythagorean fraternities and the many groups of Gnostics with their faith in secret revelations. Some of these were bloody or licentious or much involved with magic, others dignified, ethical, even ascetic. The cult of Isis, which had had a fairly abandoned past, became respectable and must have provided a haven for many of the womenfolk of the devotees of Mithraism. Although Isis was not originally a Mother Goddess in the usual sense, her cult moved in that direction and she was sometimes portrayed with the infant Horus. Among them all, at first seemingly of little importance and long overtopped by the Isis cult and Mithraism, was that Dark Horse, Christianity. While almost all other worshippers could, if they wished, be initiated into more than one Mystery and at the same time pay due patriotic honour to the State religion, the Christians, like the strict followers of Judaism from whom their founders had come, were exclusive even unto death.

Finally, penetrating almost all schools of thought and all faiths, was the astralism which had made the whole Graeco-Roman world 'much subject to skyey influences'.

Out of this turmoil the Sun God rose majestically, drawing many ideas and many divinities into his single light. It is perhaps best to approach this solar monotheism which assumed its sway in the third and fourth centuries through the emperors who gave it much support. This chronicle has already shown what frequent affinity there has been everywhere and at all times between crowned heads and sun gods. The Roman emperors must have been aware that in Assyria, Persia and Egypt royal houses had owed much to their solar divinity. The first occupant of their own imperial throne had chosen the radiant Apollo as his patron, built a temple to him on the

o   193

Palatine and dedicated his famous Pantheon to the Sun and Stars. Nero had been interested in Mithraism, and Commodus, the debauched son of the saintly Stoic, Marcus Aurelius, joined in Mithraic worship, insisting, so it is said, that the symbolic deaths that were a part of it should be turned into ritual murders (he would have enjoyed himself even more in Tenochtitlan). A bust of Commodus shows him wearing a Mithraic style Phrygian cap charged with the seven stars, while in a frieze of this time at Ephesus the Sun is taking his father Aurelius up to heaven in a chariot escorted by Moon and Stars.

Early in the next century Caracalla had his sculptors portray him in the guise of Pharaoh, and in so doing cannot have failed to think of himself as the son of the Sun God. He was in fact particularly devoted to the Lord Serapis, and contemporary inscriptions identify this life-giving divinity with Jupiter and the Sun.

After the murder of Caracalla the very next reign was an excursion into sun worship of crazy eccentricity. Such an extraordinary appearance of the Sun God cannot be left out from this history, and the account in the *Golden Bough* is so exquisite an example of Frazerian manner and attitude that I will not resist quoting it almost in full. The 'black, conical stone' immediately recalls the original *benben* at Egyptian Heliopolis.

At Emesa in Syria there was a large black conical stone which was said to have fallen from the sky and bore the Phoenician name of Elagabalus. It was popularly supposed to be an image of the Sun, and was lodged in a great temple resplendent with gold and silver and precious stones. The god received the homage not only of the natives but of distant peoples, whose governors and kings sent costly offerings every year to the shrine. Among the rest the soldiers of a great Roman camp pitched in the neighbourhood used to visit the temple and admire the handsome young priest when, wearing a jewelled crown and arrayed in gorgeous robes of purple and gold, he tripped gracefully in the dance round the altar to the melody of pipes and flutes and other musical instruments. This dainty priest of the Sun, then in the full bloom of youth and beauty, and resembling, we are told, the ideal portraits of the youthful Bacchus, was the future Emperor Elagabalus, the most abandoned reprobate who ever sat upon a throne. On being elevated, at the age of fourteen, to the imperial dignity by the intrigues of his artful grandmother and the favour of the soldiers, the stripling, whose original name was Bassianus, assumed the style of his barbarous god Elagabalus or Heliogabalus, as the name was also pronounced in order to suggest to Greek ears the name of the Sun (*Helios*). Further the young fanatic caused the rude fetish of the deity to be transported from Emesa to Rome, where he built a great and stately temple for it on the Palatine beside the imperial palace. The site had formerly been occupied by the genuine old Roman god Orcus. Round about the temple were set up many altars, on which every morning hecatombs of bulls and sheep were slaughtered, incense of all sorts was piled, and jars of the oldest and finest wines were poured, so that streams of mingled blood and wine flooded the pavement. And round the altar on the ensanguined pavement danced the emperor and a choir of Syrian damsels with clashing cymbals and droning drums, while the knights and senators stood looking on in a great circle, and the entrails of the sacrificial victims and the perfumes were carried in golden jars on the heads, not of menials and servitors, but of captains of armies and ministers of state, arrayed in the long loose-sleeved robes and linen shoes of Syrian prophets; for among these degenerate nobles it was deemed the highest honour to be allowed to participate in the sacrifice.

And in the height of summer, lest the Sun-god should suffer from the excess of his own heat, the considerate emperor escorted him to an agreeable suburb, where he had built another vast and costly temple in which the deity might while away the sultry months till the refreshing coolness of autumn should permit of his return to Rome. On these annual excursions to and from the country the god, or rather the stone, was conveyed in a chariot glittering with gold and jewels and drawn by six superb white horses, themselves resplendent in trappings of gold. No man might share the sacred chariot with the deity. But the emperor himself held the reins and went before, walking the whole way backward out of respect to the god, upon whom he kept his eyes fixed, and supported on either side by his guards lest he should stumble and fall. The whole road was thickly strewed with gold dust, and on either side ran crowds waving torches and flinging garlands and flowers on the path.

The reign of Elagabalus was solar monotheism of a kind, but hardly of the kind which seemed to be triumphing in the late third and early fourth centuries. This was advanced most directly by the brilliant soldier and administrator Aurelian, who unquestionably saw it as a means of centralizing and strengthening a now shaky empire. But he may also have had a personal reason, for his mother was rumoured to be a priestess of the sun. Ironically, it fell to Aurelian to have to destroy Palmyra, the centre of the Syrian sun worship which had been so influential in Rome. After repeated disloyalty and revolt of the Palmyrenes, he defeated them and razed their city in A.D. 272. The next year, however, he showed his sympathies by restoring the splendid Temple of the Sun. In the year 274 Aurelian instituted the cult of *Sol Invictus* as the official state religion of the Empire, setting up a pontifical college under a High Pontiff for its administration. In his own person, too, he broke with the last scruples of the republican tradition, and assumed the divinity and splendour of an oriental sovereign. He wore the diadem (which he may have recognized as a solar symbol) and assumed the title of Lord and God on his medals. This state sun worship centred on the emperor was carried yet further by Diocletian. He himself enhanced the royal pomp, not only wearing the diadem but dressing in golden robes and demanding that all who approached him should prostrate themselves. In 308, when he met fellow rulers at Carnuntum, they consecrated a temple to Mithras as patron (*fautor*) of the Empire.

Only a few years later Constantine suffered his conversion and *Sol Invictus* abruptly made way for Christ. Yet the Sun God was to have a brief and glowing resurrection. The

Emperor Julian, who had seen many of his family murdered by Christians and was deeply devoted to pagan tradition, restored the solar monotheism. He was one of those, too, who had responded most strongly to the physical power of the star. 'From my childhood', he says, 'an extraordinary longing for the rays of the God penetrated deep into my soul.' For him the solar faith was full also of moral light. In his Prayer to the Sun, a religious expression worthy to be set beside the Hymn of Akhenaten, he begs the Sun King to grant him 'a good life, more perfect understanding and a divine mind'. So successfully did he live up to his ideals that when at the head of his armies he had to stay in Antioch, then a most dissolute city, his ascetic habits seem to have caused the Christians there quite as much distress as his paganism. The story that when he lay dying, fatally wounded in battle against the Persians, he threw his blood towards heaven and cried, 'You have conquered, O Galilean', is almost certainly fiction. Another incident more truthfully, and even more movingly, symbolizes the end of the rule of the pagan Sun God in the western world.

Julian wished to revive what had been Apollo's greatest source of strength—his oracle at Delphi. For some long time now the Pythia had fallen silent. The Emperor sent one Oribasius to the shrine at Delphi where she had uttered the prophecies that had swayed the fortunes of Greece and Rome, but he came back with this message: 'Tell the King, the fair-wrought hall has fallen to the ground. No longer hath Phoebus a shelter, nor a prophetic laurel, nor a spring that speaks. The water of speech is quenched.'

This, very briefly, is the history of the solar religion of the later Roman Empire. I cannot hope to do more than hint at the meanings, so utterly various, which it must have had for men and women of countless races, creeds, philosophies and states of consciousness. In those last days of classical paganism the Sun God shone like a pharos for ships at sea, guiding them on their way or lighting them into a harbour where all conflicting ideas

197

could anchor together in a kind of harmony and mental agreement.

For the astralists a sun-centred faith was a natural enough outcome of their worship of the heavenly bodies, as the sun was so evidently the greatest of their Seven. Moreover they had been pushed further in this direction by the scientific discoveries of the Greek scientists who understood at least something of the gravitational power of the sun in the solar system. The astrological writer Julian of Laodicea declared, 'The sun has been appointed King and ruler of the universe, leading and originating all.'

Among the philosophers, the Stoics came readily into the fold. With their belief in a deified world and a world heart, in the divinity of the planets and stars and in fire as the highest and purest of the elements, the Sun God could easily be exalted. Indeed leading Stoics had recognized solar pre-eminence from the first. 'It was the opinion of Cleanthes that the Sun is the ruling power of the world . . . the Sun is the potent ruler and master of the universe.' This led easily to seeing the sun as 'the heart of the world', 'the eye of the world', or as Macrobius had it, the mind of the world—'*Sol mundi mens est.*' Also the platonizing Stoic, Posidonius, in wholeheartedly accepting the principles of astrology had done much to unite the ideas of philosophers and astronomers into a cosmic mysticism.

Inevitably the solar religion came into conflict with the transcendental outlook of Platonists and Neo-Platonists. But reconciliation was not difficult. Plato himself had idealized sun worship and called the sun the 'offspring of the first god'. His followers, although they saw the One God as above and outside the visible universe, could still readily accept the sun as the supreme symbol of this spiritual sun. God was 'the Sun's Sun' who 'causes the visible rays to shine upon him who sees. . . . For as the rising sun dissipates the darkness and floods all things with light, so when God, the Intelligible Sun, rises and shines on the soul, the darkness of passion and evil is dissipated.' Even

Julian the Apostate's theology recognized three aspects of the solar divinity—the Sun of the Intelligible World, of the Intelligent World, and of the Sensible World—which last he identified with Mithras.

As for the Establishment and its institutional religion, the Sun God could be accepted without a qualm. For one thing the emperors had led the way and the throne was deeply involved. For another the sky gods had always been supreme, Apollo glorious and Jupiter an All Father with monotheizing tendencies who could become the Sun at the drop of a hat.

Finally, so great was the appeal of solar adoration, and perhaps also the longing for synthesis and religious unity, that many of the Mystery cults also capitulated. Mithraism was, of course, in a special position, for with a kind of historical justice, its Persian divinity with his long Indo-European lineage was now himself patron of the Empire. But the initiates of many other Mysteries proved willing to identify their particular deity with this central light.

Those who did not were the Christians. Their refusal ever to compromise in matters of worship was undoubtedly one of the best reasons for their final success. Others were the moral universe of Judaism, the admission of women, an able and centralized leadership and the proclamation of a Founder who had at once fulfilled Messianic prophecy and himself lived out the myth of the dying and resurrected god of so many Mystery religions. But it would be presumption and folly for me to attempt to isolate what was unique in Christianity. That is already understood by each according to his understanding. Rather it is my business here to show how far solar concepts and practices were continued in the churches and among the people, partly by direct historical synthesis, partly through man's innate psychological tendency to identify both morality and spiritual illumination with light, and hence irresistibly with the source of light and life in the physical world.

Since the earliest days the Christians had been intensely

chiliastic, daily prepared for the end of the world and the judgment of souls. Yet perhaps few people are wholly desirous of such an end, so that the continued smooth working of the solar system proved no set-back. Instead of the Second Coming the Christians were ready to accept the conversion of Constantine, and instead of the next world temporal power and glory in this one. As he himself and all his house had been devoted to sun worship, it is not surprising that the vision which preceded the Emperor's conversion was of a fiery cross appearing to him at noonday. Here again was the sun symbol which has already been followed back to the pastoralists of Bronze Age Britain and on to the haloes of later Christian iconography.

The Christians of the first three centuries had denied the tolerance and compromise of other faiths, had gladly suffered horrible martyrdoms for refusing a pinch of incense to the imperial altars. Yet with the malicious irony so often apparent in history, even while they fought heroically on one front, their position was infiltrated from another. Once it became evident that the end of the world was to be delayed, the original message and the social and ethical pattern of the little Christian communities were not enough to make headway in the competitive religious world of the day. No more than a bird can build its nest exclusively with its own feathers could the Christian leaders build a faith, rites and church without picking up all manner of extraneous material from the Graeco-Roman environment.

Already, as has appeared, Judaism had been affected by the spiritualized solar vision of Persia, and this element was strong among the Essenes who may have had such direct influence on the first generation of Christians. Certainly the kind of language used in the Fourth Gospel must have helped many worshippers of the Intelligible Sun to cross the border into Christianity with scarcely more effort or change of scene than that experienced by a traveller going from Monmouthshire into Wales. The early fathers, who in general were concerned to harmonize Christ with Greek philosophy rather than with the Mysteries, used this kind of language too. Origen says, 'He opened the gates of Light to those who had been the sons of darkness and of night.' They also had to come to terms with astralism. While all from Paul onwards declared that Christians could not be subject to the astral powers, the stars had to be brought into the picture. Thus Origen taught that sun, moon and stars worshipped Christ, and that he had died for them as well as for mankind. 'He did not die on behalf of men only but on behalf of all other rational beings . . . such as the stars.' Jesus himself said that he 'must needs be crucified and taste death for the universe'.

Another idea which the Christians absorbed as naturally as the air they breathed was that the deity dwelt above their heads in the furthest celestial realms. Paul taught that men had a pneumatic body that could ascend to immortality 'where Christ is'. In spite of the reticence of the gospels on the Ascension, literal belief in it soon led to the making of innumerable pictures of Christ ascending into the skies either in an aureole or in a fiery chariot of evident solar ancestry.

Perhaps most of all Christianity became involved with the Sun God through Mithraism and through the solar monotheism in which it culminated. For all its success with the mass of the people, Christianity could not be satisfied with coming to terms with Greek thought and the theories of astrology. More and more it had to lean towards the Mystery religions with their initiations and sacramental means to personal salvation. And it was with Mithraism, its greatest rival among the Mysteries, that Christianity came to have most in common. Some of these similarities came from a sharing of oriental sources, others perhaps from direct borrowing. That they were striking enough to cause embarrassment the following list will show:[1] 'The fraternal and democratic spirit of the first communities; the identification of the object of adoration with light and the sun; the legends of shepherds and their gifts, of the flood and the

[1] From *Encyclopaedia Britannica*, 11th edition, Vol. XVIII, p. 624.

ark; the representation in art of the fiery chariot; the drawing of water from the rock; the use of bell, book and candle, holy water and the communion, the sanctification of Sunday and the 25th December; the insistence on moral conduct . . . the doctrine of heaven and hell, of the mediation of the Logos, the atoning sacrifice, the warfare between good and evil and the triumph of the former, the immortality of the soul, the last judgment, the resurrection of the body and the fiery destruction of the universe . . .'

All these similarities led to bitter recriminations on both sides, especially during those final decades of their rivalry. Just as nearly a millennium and a half later the Christians were to blame the similarities between their doctrines and those of sun-worshippers in the New World on the devil, so did they now. Even so early a writer as Justin could declare 'the wicked demons have imitated [the Eucharist] in the mysteries of Mithras, commanding that the same thing be done'.

But from the time of Constantine the confusion became much greater. During its short-lived triumph as the state religion of Rome Mithraism had been set up with its elaborate sacerdotal system—its High Pontiff and the rest. Some of these forms were taken over when Christianity succeeded Mithraism. A devout Christian historian has said how when it became the state religion 'the Empire was partly christianized and the church partly paganized', and 'Christ succeeded to the place vacated by Serapis and Mithra, and the Madonna gradually to the place vacated by Isis and the Great Mother'.

I do not think it would be an exaggeration to say that in the fourth century and for some time afterwards there was for very many people of the western Empire a total confusion between state Christianity and the state sun worship it displaced. Members of the eastern church indeed taunted those of the western with being no better than pagan sun-worshippers. The choice of 25th December for Christ's Nativity gave especial trouble, for it was the day of the winter solstice when the

Brumalia was celebrated, the feast of the birth of the Unconquered Sun. Paulinus wrote:

> For it is after the solstice, when Christ born in the flesh with
> the new sun transformed the season of cold winter, and vouch-
> safing to mortal man a healing dawn, commanded the nights to
> decrease at his coming with advancing day.

In the Roman Catholic church the Great Antiphon, sung on
21st December, pleads:

> O Day-spring, Brightness of the Light eternal, and Sun of
> Justice, come and enlighten those who sit in darkness and the
> shadow of death.

The decision to make the Nativity of Christ coincide with
the *Natalis Invicti Soli* meant that pagans and Christians were
holding simultaneous festivals, and although the Christians
insisted that while the actual sun would wane once more
'Holy Church celebrates the festival of the Nativity of Christ,
the Sun of Righteousness, who begins to conquer error and
Satan and will never wane', blurring of the two celebrations
was inevitable. Augustine had to exhort the brethren not to
solemnize the day on account of the sun like the heathen, but
rather on account of him who made the sun. Leo the Great
rebuked those who thought that Christmas was observed for
the solstice and not the nativity of Christ.

Much of the rest of the early Christian Year runs side by
side with the cycle of the sun. Thus after the Nativity at the
winter solstice, Easter is on the Sunday following the first full
moon after the Vernal Equinox, an appropriate date to celebrate the Resurrection. The rite of the candles, each proclaimed
as the 'light of Christ', and the lighting of the large Paschal
Taper with the accompanying words of the *Exultet*, 'Rejoice,
O earth, illumined by this celestial radiancy', has solar associations. The Taper burns until Ascension Day, and this whole
period celebrates the renewal of life and the final triumph of
light over darkness. In addition to this solar pattern of the

Christian year, there was the naming of Sunday as the holy day of the Christian week.

When all these parallels are remembered, all either in being or foreshadowed by the fourth century, and when, too, it is known that for many of the more conscious of the former worshippers of *Sol Invictus* the physical sun had been seen as the symbol (itself divine, certainly) of the One God, then my statement that there was for some a near identity between the two faiths is surely justified. By now the Sun God as the Sun of Justice and the Sun of Righteousness is familiar. In this light (I choose the phrase intentionally) a dramatic discovery made below the present dome of St. Peter's at Rome is not surprising. After his adoption of Christianity the Emperor Constantine ordered the building of the new basilica of St. Peter's on the Vatican Hill, a plan which involved covering over a cemetery part pagan and part Christian. When in the 1950's excavations were made below the cathedral in the hope of finding the tomb of St. Peter, this necropolis was found and in it the earliest known Christian mosaic. It showed Christ as Sun God driving a chariot with flying cloak and a rayed nimbus behind his head.

In its earliest days as a world religion, then, Christianity had absorbed much from more than one historical source of sun worship. In the Catholic churches the symbolism has very largely remained. It is present everywhere—in church building and church furniture and in many of the ritual enactments of the Christian year. Undoubtedly as the tradition of the worship of *Sol Invictus* of the late Roman Empire was left behind the overlapping of ideas became far less, and for most Christians the use of solar imagery, both visual and verbal, has been accepted in a more and more purely symbolic sense. On the other hand, among peasants and all the simpler members of the flock, many of the practices of sun cults long remained, most of them clustering round May Day, midsummer and Christmas. There were the May Day Beltane Fires of Celtic lands, pro-

VII. CHRIST AS HELIOS: mosaic below the High Altar in St Peter's, Rome
From THE KINGDOMS OF CHRIST *by P. Bamm (Thames & Hudson)*

bably descended from remote Indo-European tradition; there was the rolling of cheeses, huge cakes or actual burning wheels down hillsides—usually to give the sun energy at midsummer. The Yule Log and fiery pudding of the English Christmas, the crown of candles of the Swedish St. Lucia festival, are rites of the winter solstice. The St. George's play of the Christmas mummers was an enactment of the solar cycle. The Germanic Christmas-tree, introduced into Britain by that believer in the scientific attitude, Prince Albert, was perhaps the best of all folk expressions of the idea of the return of light out of darkness which was the essential meaning of the winter festival, the birthday of the Unconquered Sun.

I have said that for the educated Christian solar imagery has become increasingly symbolic, less affected by historical memories of the worship of the sun. But if, as I hope, I have succeeded in keeping alive in these pages the actual psychic meanings underlying religious myths and imagery, then this historical statement will appear oversimple. For while in the outer world of passing centuries the Sun God might be waning, in the mental world of the individual consciousness he could never set. For this is the secret discovered beyond doubt by studies of the psyche, that the individual projects from the unconscious an image of his unified and divine self as a sun figure. There is an inner sun of the vault of the mind corresponding to the outer in the vault of heaven.

Countless mental patients have seen it in dream images and fantasies, sometimes in crude libidinous forms with arms and legs and phallus. When all over the world children draw a radiant sun face beside a house, the picture has risen from within their minds as much as it has been remembered. They are in fact expressing the same inner vision which may be seen as Christ and Mother Church, as the radiant Sun God and the containing Mother Goddess.

For the mystics of all faiths, who have undertaken spiritual exercises to reconcile conscious with unconscious, the light of the spirit and intellect with the darkness of life, this light appears as a radiance, sometimes diffuse, sometimes as a disk Thus the tenth-century Symeon describes his mystic vision of the One and the Many: 'It is not separated when it becomes many, but remains undivided, and it is in me, and rises in my poor heart like a sun or circular disk of the sun, like light, for it is light.' A century later Hildegarde of Bingen records, 'the light I see is not local, but is everywhere, and brighter far than the cloud which supports the sun'.

So it is easy to see how the sun imagery of Christianity could be constantly renewed. That it is always renewed the simplest observation will show. As well as the persistence of such accepted iconography as the sun monstrance and the radiant cross of Christ Risen or Christ in Glory and the nimbus, it appears often in less formalized expressions. On the crowded, turbulent west fronts of Spanish churches in Mexico I have noticed the sun and moon carved among other Christian symbols; in Prague, I think along a street leading uphill to the cathedral, I remember seeing fine baroque figures of Christ standing upon the sun, the Virgin Mary upon the moon. I find that in the still-building Coventry cathedral there is a sculpture of the radiant sun drawn as a child draws it. And only yesterday, walking round Lichfield cathedral, to my astonishment (for I am not well versed in these things), on a staid little early nineteenth-century plaque I saw the dove of the Holy Ghost not only surrounded by the usual radiant light but enclosed within the ring of a tail-swallowing serpent. Again and again the sun appears within domes, for these were often a conscious symbol at once for the heavens and for the dome of the skull—the house of divine radiance.

That the imagery persisted also round Christian thrones is still evident. Surely (although I have not seen it admitted) the many-pointed golden crown is solar, and the imperial form with the crossing hoops also? It will be recalled that Archbishop Fisher had to mark the crown to get the cardinal points right

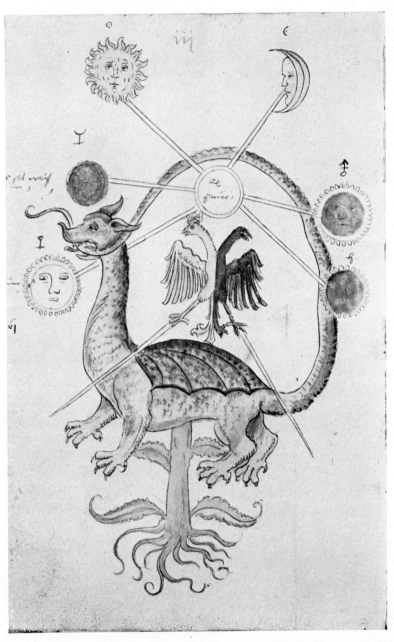

VIII. FROM A SIXTEENTH-CENTURY MS OF DE ALCHIMIA

when placing it on the head of Queen Elizabeth II. The golden solar robe as part of the coronation vestments I have already mentioned. The best secularized example is of course Louis XIV, whose inflated ego would certainly have had no difficulty in allowing him to see himself as the *Roi Soleil*, radiant as Apollo. Then again those solar creatures, the lion and eagle, have had their place in the arms of most royal houses. The bird has even been strong enough to transfer himself to represent that supposedly anti-royalist republic, the United States of America.

Most clearly of all solar imagery persisted, and was even developed, in alchemy, that strange blend of semi-magical chemistry with Christian and astrological symbolism. Anyone who has even got as far as hearing Jonson's *Alchemist* will know from the lips of his impostor that *Sol* was much invoked. There seems no doubt that while many of these misguided gentlemen were messing about with retorts trying to turn mercury and other substances into gold, others knew in a confused kind of way that they were dealing also with religious symbols, that all their terms had double meanings. Each 'planet' had its metal, and that of the sun was, inevitably, gold. The alchemist's stone was often identified with Christ, and gold with some spiritual value. It was the incorruptible stuff of salvation. The illustrations of alchemical works are full of the most astounding solar and other celestial figures, some directly inherited from astrology, others directly projected from the psyches of the alchemists themselves.

They also made much use of symbols of the mandala form. With mandalas, which take the form of a cruciform composition within a ring, or more elaborately, a radiate form such as compass, star, flower or sun, I am back once more with the sun wheel and the symbol of the cardinal points so powerful in pre-Columban America. With crowns and cakes, cheeses and burning wheels bouncing down hillsides; with the sun disks in Bronze Age graves. Before I had ever heard of the mandala, at a time of intense emotional stress, I drew a most characteristic one myself. So I have some understanding of how they arise in the psyche. They are used deliberately by Buddhists and Hindus as objects of contemplation, and they are produced as part of their cure by mental patients. They relate to effort to integrate conscious with unconscious, light with darkness.

A few people are fascinated by these ever-shifting forms of psychic symbolism. One of them, hearing I was writing a book on Man and the Sun, said he supposed it would all be about mandalas. But many more people, and at most times I am among them, find this whole realm of thought, feeling and experience oppressive and even tedious. It means living mentally in a kaleidoscopic world (that mandala image again). Quite soon one becomes giddy. Moreover, I set out to write of Man and the Sun in the outside world of history and not in this timeless inner world. If every now and then I issue a reminder that the inner forms exist and are often the seed of the outer growths, that is enough. Anyone who is either sceptical of, or wants to know more about, these images of the unconscious and their expression in alchemy, astrology and religious symbolism, particularly solar symbolism, can consult Dr. Jung's *Secret of the Golden Flower*, *Psychology and Alchemy*, and the opening of his *Symbols of Transformation*. The pictures alone should be enough to shake the sceptic.

I have now to complete this very considerable part of my book which has been concerned with the history of sun worship. It has of necessity been selective, because the mass of material is so great. I had, for instance, thought of including a whole chapter on the cult in Japanese Shintoism. It is distinguished by being centred on a goddess in place of the almost universal god (others were honoured in Syria and among the Hittites), and by the fact that in the Mikado a sun king of Bronze Age style survived in a modern, industrialized state. The Sun Goddess, Amaterasu, of dazzling beauty, came from the left eye of the first creator god, just as her husband the moon came from the right. A circular mirror, reflecting her own light, was her usual symbol. Her grandson became the first sovereign of Japan, and she was in this sense recognized as the mother of the Mikado just as Re was father of Pharaoh and Inti of the Sapa Inca. She was undoubtedly already being worshipped in the eighth century A.D., and probably as early as the second millennium B.C., so that there may be an unbroken inheritance from the Bronze Age. Until recently pilgrims flocked to her great shrine at Ise. So much did this supreme deity of Japan retain her powers that she was able to place her symbol, a boldly rayed sun disk, on the national flag. It is, so far as I know, the only modern flag in which a solar symbol provides the whole design.

There would be good reasons for devoting space to Amaterasu, but at this stage it would be intolerable to return to myths replete with divine eyes, mirrors, spears, the goddess sulking in a cave and so forth. But to give some idea of the actual practice of sun worship in Japan within recent times, I will quote from Revon's *Le Shintoisme*. The Japanese love of natural life, of birds and flowers and gardens, and the sense of man's harmony with them, already suggest that in this respect at least their worship of the sun had something in common with that of Akhenaten. The following description helps, I think, to confirm this similarity.

The Japanese people adore the Sun as a living god; the worship which they pay him is not vague and spiritual, it is direct and absolutely real, when, every morning, the glorious luminary rises in face of his worshipper, lighting up and warming all things, or at evening when he is about to plunge into the night. And such is the inward, instinctive faith of the whole religious public, from the artisan who, from the back of his dark shop, turns towards the bright dawn, claps his hands and recites piously his prayer to the goddess, up to the pilgrim who, on the summit of Mount Fujiyama, prostrates himself, with dazzled eyes, before the first golden shafts of light and worships the orb with forehead bowed down to the rocks. For my part, I must confess that one morning on the summit of Fuji, perceiving myself alone in a scene which might have befitted the Last Judgment, faced by the radiant orb which seemed to me like the last living thing of creation, I had a lively illusion that it was a personal being; and when, a moment afterwards, I saw pilgrims hasting from all sides to adore him, I thought their faith perfectly natural.

It is not difficult to pass from this account of the 'direct and absolutely real' adoration of Amaterasu to the final scene in this chronicle, to sun worship in the modern West. The hasting pilgrims might well be the tourists and other more wealthy sun-seekers crowding off to the Mediterranean, to Jamaica, Miami or Arizona.

Our civilization is almost wholly secularized, having lost its symbolic dimension and its guiding myths. That was the meaning of Nietzsche's cry 'God is dead'. That a hidden craving for them is still there is shown by occasional outbreaks such as that roused by the Coronation in 1953, when sane and sober men declared that these ancient rituals had brought about the spiritual rebirth of the West. But in general they have burnt out, and for the present no phoenix has presented itself.

Instead we find our apparently secular substitutes. The cult of the sun is certainly one of the more important. Millions of men, women and children of all classes and many types go to places, usually the edge of the sea, held suitable for their secular rites. They buy vast quantities of oils, greases and lotions to anoint, not as of old the *benben* or other sacred images, but their own bodies. They don strange dark spectacles and strip off their clothes. No less than former worshippers, they are prepared to suffer. Strong men make themselves ill, women ruin their complexions, children get sunstroke. Since the cult began acres of skin must have crusted and peeled, exposing areas of pink and white ruin surely as painful as the gashes of the Aztecs. Yet day after day they return to worship, determined to gain the tan which is the proof of salvation.

Among all these millions there must be many who could say with Julian the Apostate, 'From my childhood an extraordinary

longing for the rays of the god penetrated deep into my soul.'
I do not doubt that there is an element of mysticism in all these
practices, though not many initiates would be as conscious of it
as D. H. Lawrence shows himself to be in his short story, *Sun*.
Nudists, presumably, must share in it. And it is there because
the sun in our skies has always been able to invoke such feeling
in the bodies and minds it has created out of rock and water.
Quite simply, the sun has been the agent of our long creation,
and we know it.

Meanwhile the travel agencies, far more cynical than any
priesthood, pile up their gold. They cover their pamphlets with
sun images bright with rays and happy-faced. And when the
worshippers reach the beaches and the gardens do they not
place themselves under huge, many-quartered umbrellas? Perhaps they, too, are solar symbols—sun wheels, mandalas. ...

CHRISTIAN MONSTRANCE

SUN OF INTELLECT

I HAVE FOLLOWED DOWN to the present day a very ancient form of man's relationship with the sun. That of worship and mystical union. I have now to take a short step back in time in order to see the beginning of an altogether new relationship—that of cool observation of the star as a physical object. The ability to achieve this was a part of that development in human consciousness which, as has already been seen, was well under way by the middle of the last millennium before Christ. This heightening of consciousness, this greater detachment of the light half of the mind and its intellectual exercises, everywhere led to questioning and change. But while in oriental lands through the Buddha and Lao Tse it led men to look inward and cultivate modes of re-establishing harmony in the psyche, and in much of the Graeco-Roman world to the founding of cults and churches for individual salvation through sacrament, in some Hellenic lands, and among a few individuals everywhere, it encouraged men instead to turn outwards and direct the power of their intellects, like searchlight beams, to illumine the surrounding universe.

In the Greek colonies of Ionia, and especially in the wealthy mercantile city of Miletus, this light was mainly focused on material nature, and so gave to the Ionian thinkers an extraordinary pre-eminence in the natural sciences. In Athens

Socrates and his followers were more concerned with man himself and with methods of thought and kinds of knowledge, and therefore gained an extraordinary pre-eminence in philosophy. With both, of course, detached reason, 'enlightenment', was supreme. I have said that it is fortunate for the structure of this book that the god Apollo was the patron both of Ionia and of Socrates. It makes it more than ever appropriate to distinguish this type of rational thought as Apollonian, and to recognize the Sun God, who has already appeared as the Sun of Life, of Justice and of Righteousness, as being also the Sun of Intellect.

From this time, then, the minds which the sun had fostered on earth were not only to worship the sun, but also to observe it. To the religious bonds by which men had mentally united the solar system, there were now to be added the scientific. What had been a god or the symbol of a god had become a body to be charted, measured, weighed, chemically analysed and finally imitated. Intellectual light was turned back upon solar light.

Ionia is accepted as the cradle of science as we understand it, yet long before its rise priests working for quite different ends had accumulated knowledge which was directly used by the Greeks. Astrology, growing out of the celestial worship of the Babylonians, had brought about a closer intimacy with the heavens. By the eighth century B.C., almost every city in the Tigris–Euphrates valley had its observatory, where Chaldeans watched and recorded the movements of sun, moon, planets and stars in their bright, unclouded skies. This they did partly to regulate the holy calendar and to harmonize the cycles of the sun and moon for its seasonal feasts, partly to advise the King of Assyria and other rulers concerning the 'Skyey influences'. In this way they learnt of the *Saros*, the cycle of just over eighteen years in which eclipses of the sun and moon repeat themselves.

Thales, who was born in Miletus in about 640 B.C., is now recognized as the founder of the Ionian school, and in his own day was honoured as the chief of the Seven Wise Men of Greece. It so happens that he won much of his tremendous fame in the ancient world for his correct prediction of a solar eclipse, probably for the year 585 B.C. The sun was in fact completely obscured during a battle between the Lydians and Medes, and the combatants felt such awe that they stopped fighting and made a lasting peace. It is reasonably certain that Thales owed this impressive coup, one of the earliest instances of the admiration felt for science because it works in action, to knowledge of the *Saros* acquired from the Chaldeans. He himself visited Egypt, and although in that devout land astrolatry had never evolved into astronomy, he seems to have gone to the priests for lessons in geometry which would later have aided the Ionians in astronomical measurement. So did the ancient world of Bronze Age lore contribute to the new world of science.

Thales deserves even further distinction here for having been, so far as is known, the first man on earth to claim that the moon depended upon the sun for its light. Hitherto, although the sun had usually been hailed as the greater, they had been regarded more or less as on an equal footing—expressed in their mythological relationship of husband and wife or brother and sister. Thales made great advances, yet his cosmology was primitive; he saw the universe as a hollow hemisphere floating on infinite waters. His pupil Anaximander's views, though quite different, were hardly nearer to the truth, but he is noteworthy here for having introduced the gnomon into Greece for fixing solstices, and also, it is said, the time-keeping sundial. After him the ability of the Ionians and the soundness of their natural philosophy seemed already to be declining before the destruction of their state by the Persians. Thus Xenophanes, an exile from Ionia, taught that the sun and stars were newly created each day, and Heraclitus, a native of Ephesus of amazing arrogance, held the sun to measure a foot across and to be daily rekindled.

Far more fortunate in his speculations was Anaxagoras, a devoted philosopher who was born in Asia Minor in about 500 B.C. At that time Athens was rising as the chief focus of Hellenic thought, and he went to live there, becoming a dear friend of Pericles. His ideas on the creation of the universe pointed towards a sound atomic theory, while he saw all heavenly bodies other than the sun as fragments of rock torn from the earth and ignited by the speed of their rotation. As for the sun itself he described it as a mass of blazing metal, larger than the Peloponnese. It was probably most of all this explanation of the nature of the divine sun that roused the priests against him and led to his trial for blasphemy. Although Pericles succeeded in getting him acquitted, he had to return to Asia Minor for his last years. So Anaxagoras became the first to suffer at least a mild martyrdom on behalf of a scientific explanation of the solar system.

While the speculations of many of the Ionian school were wide of the mark or even rather foolish, all remained true to the scientific attitude. They accepted the material unity of the cosmos and of all life and sought to explain their workings by detached observation and reason. Their main trouble was that they still lacked the techniques to enable them to confirm or reject their theories, so that one appeared as good as another and there could be no steady progress or even approximate finality.

Meanwhile another school was founded which forsook the scientific way and became involved in mysticism. Pythagoras was probably born in the island of Samos and so came from the fringes of Ionia, but he soon went to the Greek colony of Crotona in southern Italy where he founded the brotherhood that was to have so great an influence in the Graeco-Roman world. Pythagoras, then, a brilliant mathematician and a mystic preoccupied with souls and their destiny, has a place half-way between man's religious relationship with the sun and his scientific one. Yet the strictly astronomical views of the

Master and his followers were hardly less scientific than those of the Ionians. Indeed, they demand an honoured place in this chapter as some two millennia later Copernicus was to declare that it was their ideas that first led his thoughts in the right direction. The Pythagoreans were the first to conceive that the earth was a globe held in space which, together with the planets, revolved round a central luminary. Curiously, however, they did not allow the sun to be this centre, but a fire which they named Hestia, the hearth fire of the universe, or the watch tower of Zeus (the Ionians, plainly, would never have used names of this kind). Thales had taught that the moon reflected the sun, but the Pythagoreans held that both sun and moon reflected the blaze from Hestia. Ten bodies, supported in crystal spheres, revolved round the central fire, first the Antichthon or counter-earth, then earth itself followed in sequence by the moon, the sun, the five known planets and finally the fixed stars. Men could not see Hestia or the Antichthon because the side of the globe on which they lived was always turned away from them, light and heat coming to them by reflection from the sun. When sun and earth were both on the same side of the central fire the inhabited side of the earth was turned towards the sun and it was day; when they were on opposite sides the populated face was away from the sun and it was night. Combining this harmoniously revolving universe with their musical knowledge, the Pythagoreans hit upon the charming notion of the music of the spheres. They believed that as the spheres revolved they emitted sweet sounds, lower notes nearer Hestia where their speed was less and progressively higher ones the further out their orbit and the greater the rate of spin. Together they sounded the cosmic octave. This music was only inaudible to human beings because their ears were so accustomed to it that they could no longer distinguish it from silence.

The fourth-century Heraclides deserves a place in this story because, as a result presumably of both observation and calculation, he formed the opinion that though the sun went round the earth, it was itself the centre of the orbits of Mercury and Venus. This Heraclides, who had come from Pontus, became a respected member of Plato's Academy—not an institution which is generally associated with the scientific attitude. Plato himself stood by the old commonsense view of the earth as the fixed centre of the universe, and unhappily for the progress of astronomy and man's understanding of his dependence on the sun, so too did Aristotle. Aristotle, however, with his more scientific approach to nature, accepted with modification the elaborate system of Eudoxus, the earliest mathematical theory of celestial appearances, which involved no fewer than twenty-six or twenty-seven variously interlocking orbits. This Aristotelian cosmology with no very great modification was accepted by most Christian and other thinkers for the next eighteen hundred years.

Meanwhile, however, the spirit of the Ionians had been more truly maintained by Alexandria, now becoming the greatest centre of science and learning in all the Mediterranean. In such a cosmopolitan city there was little fear of priestly interference with the freedom of thought. It was here, in the years before the middle of the third century B.C., that Aristarchus observed the heavens and made the deductions which establish him as one of the heroes of this part of my narrative. He was the first man on earth to claim, and with remarkable certainty, that the earth went round the sun. He is quoted by Archimedes as having declared that the fixed stars and the sun remained motionless while the earth circled the sun, making the journey in the course of a year. He accepted the view that the earth daily revolved on its own axis.

In addition, Aristarchus looked dispassionately at those ancient divinities the sun and moon, and determined to measure them and their distances with no more sense of impiety than if he had been concerned with the volume of the Great Pyramid or the distance between Alexandria and Memphis.

The method he chose to calculate how far the sun was from the earth relative to the moon was by measuring the angle between their centres when just half the moon was bright. In principle this was sound, and although the lack of instruments made an exact estimate of half-moon impossible, leading Aristarchus to say that the sun was not more than twenty times more distant when in fact it is four hundred, the error was not, after all, colossal within astronomical limits, and the correctness of the general approach was impeccable.

In Athens Cleanthes the Stoic (nicknamed the Ass), whose faith in the divinity of the sun has already appeared, accused Aristarchus of impiety. Even Archimedes decided in favour of an earth-centred universe, while not condemning the bolder theory. Probably the enduring authority of Aristotle would have ensured that Western man would go into the Middle Ages confident that he lived at the centre of things; it was made quite certain when the eminent astronomer Hipparchus gave it the support of his vast prestige. This man, who had his observatory in Rhodes, birthplace of the Sun God Helios, and worked there during the latter half of the second century B.C., made immense advances in his science. Initiating trigonometry, he placed the whole study of the heavens on a sound geometrical basis, he invented or improved instruments of measurement, including the astrolabe, and drew up a great catalogue of stars classified by magnitudes. He discovered much about the sun and its apparent movements, including the place of its apogee and the eccentricity of the orbit—the precession of the equinox which he announced in 130 B.C. He knew far more about the sun and earth than ninety-nine per cent of us today. Yet in spite of all this he still believed that the globe supporting himself and his observatory was fixed at the centre of his system. Two and a half centuries later Hipparchus's scheme of the universe was further perfected by the great systematizer, Ptolemy, who devised ingenious explanations to account for inconsistencies. The whole long episode is a warning as to how far science can go in building elaborate, detailed and convincing arguments on completely erroneous premises.

If the right judgment of Aristarchus had been immediately recognized and accepted, what difference might it have made to the history of Western man? The profoundly man-centred cosmology and theology of Christianity (derived from Judaism and enhanced) has surely been harmful. Literal belief in the idea that sun, moon, stars and all life on earth were created for man, and that the One God should know self-sacrifice on his behalf, must have encouraged the past aggressiveness and intolerance of Christians. I prefer the humble place accepted by most primitives, the Sumerian conviction that men were made as slaves for the gods, or the wayward, often jocular relationship of gods and men in classical paganism. But it is very doubtful whether knowledge of the earth's dependence on the sun would have had much effect on the Christian outlook. It would have been held, and in a sense rightly, that whatever arrangement God had made it was the best for mankind. Still, it might have been a little chastening, just as it might have strengthened the position of the late Roman worshippers of *Sol Invictus*. It would certainly have saved men from identifying their self-esteem with a geocentric universe, and have avoided the damaging clash between churchmen and scientists inevitable by the time of Galileo. Speculation of historical might-have-beens is considered disreputable, I know, but it is always interesting.

Ptolemy had no successors, for thinking men were now, as the last chapter made plain, turning from scientifically discovered explanations of the universe to those religiously revealed. The Sun of Intellect had set, and was not to rise again until the Renaissance.

This was the period when across the Atlantic Maya priests were making the observations which enabled them to perfect their calendar, establish their equivalent of the *Saros*, chart the movements of Venus and much beside. But as their own ends were religious and mystical, and their researches could not be tributary to the main stream of the Old World, they have no place here.

Alexandria was finally eclipsed with the Arab conquest of 641, when such scientific initiative as there was passed to the Arab world. Yet even there the *Almagest* and other works of Ptolemy were accepted as gospel. A fine observatory was founded at Baghdad, and later, under Arab influence, another at Maraga in Persia and a third in Samarkhand. But of all the useful if essentially minor studies made by Arab astronomers only one demands notice in an outline of solar science. Ibn Junis, working in Egypt during the eleventh century, meticulously observed two eclipses of the sun, the first to be recorded with absolute accuracy.

The Arabs' conquest of Spain, however, helped to kindle the new light of European science. It was they who made Toledo a place of astronomical research, and the Alphonsine tables issued from that city in the thirteenth century inspired further work in England and Germany. Among this was an elegant explanation, due to the English Roger Bacon and others, of the single and double rainbow—that enchanting little gift of the sun to man. Yet the work of the period was vitiated by being based on error: the unquestioning acceptance of a fixed and central earth. Indeed much of it was no more than desperate efforts to make good the inconsistencies in the Ptolemaic system which astronomy continued to reveal. It has been said that the expert is one who avoids all minor errors on the way to the grand fallacy.

The true revolution was meanwhile hatching in Italy, where the renaissance of Apollonian thought was producing a fine disrespect for the authority of the past. It was well expressed by Leonardo da Vinci when he declared that 'whoever evokes authority for his reasoning is using not his intelligence but his memory'. Leonardo also set down in one of his notebooks the stark statement 'The sun does not move'—a proof that he and other courageous minds were already opposing the Aristotelian tyranny.

The new doctrines were often referred to as Pythagorean—for no one had as yet recalled the opinions of Aristarchus. Pythagorean teaching offered the idea of the earth as one among the other planets orbiting round a point of light and heat. It remained only to substitute the visible sun for the invisible fire. From the first the Italian investigators seem to have kept their mental revolution largely underground, knowing that they would be in trouble with the orthodox. One of those to spread such dangerous, Pythagorean, thoughts was Novara. They were eagerly taken up by a young Pole, Nicolas Copernicus, who was among his students at Bologna during the closing years of the fifteenth century.

Copernicus was a mathematician, and it was probably the greater economy and elegance of the heliocentric system that appealed to him most strongly. In order to explain the many inconsistencies of the Aristotelian and Ptolemaic cosmos, a hideously complicated pattern of celestial orbits had by now been devised. Once the sun had been accepted as axial point of a solar system most of these devices could be forgotten.

For many years Copernicus hesitated to publish his work, partly because he knew how violently it would be opposed by Aristotelians in general and the Church in particular, partly, perhaps, from a genuine fear of impiety. It was published at last in Nuremberg in 1543, with a preface seeking to placate the orthodox by insisting on the hypothetical nature of the argument which had been anonymously inserted by the theologian Osiander. However, there was nothing compromising about the text of *The Revolution of the Heavenly Bodies*—one of the boldest landmarks in the whole realm of solar science. The first edition contained an illustration looking very much like a target, with rings moving in from that of the 'immobile sphere of the fixed stars', through those of Saturn, Jove, Mars, Earth with its Moon, Venus, Mercury and finally, the bull's-eye in the

form of the solar symbol of a ring round a dot used by alchemists and others, vigorously inscribed *Sol*. It was clearly set
out that Earth and the five planets orbited the sun, each in its
own 'year', and, moreover, that our own globe revolved on
its axis every twenty-four hours. The message was the same as
that of Aristarchus except that the order of the planets had been
corrected, and that it was supported by powerful mathematical
proofs.

It was indeed a tremendous mental revolution, not only in
itself but in its total upset of common sense. Men were now
gaining such faith in the new power of the human intellect, that
they were prepared to follow it against the prompting of their
senses. Ready to believe that the sun did not move across the
heavens as it could be seen to do, that the solid earth was not
fixed, that all mankind was being spun round in space at some
bewildering rate. And where, now, were Heaven and Hell? It
might still be just possible to conceive of an ascension towards
the fixed stars—but Hell? It lay where in truth it had always
lain, deep in the inner world of every individual.

As for the writing itself, it is in an ornate humanist style long
vanished from scientific literature. In the final peroration
Copernicus praises the sun as master of the universe and the
perfect work of a divine architect. 'The earth conceives from
the sun,' he says, and 'the sun rules the family of stars.'

I have said that the illustration of the Copernican system
looks like a target, and this fact calls attention to one major
error—apart from the inevitable placing of the stars in a single
fixed sphere—the assumption that in their journeys round the
sun the planets described a perfect circle.

The printed volume of *The Revolution of the Heavenly Bodies*
reached Frauenburg only just in time, so it is said, to be put into
Copernicus's dying hand. He had suffered a stroke at the end of
the previous year, and died in May of 1543. The man who
beyond others had correctly interpreted man's physical relationship with the sun, the cause of his days and nights, his familiar

seasons, wrote mainly as a mathematician for his peers. That is why his book did not cause an immediate storm. Yet even while it penetrated the thought of other mathematicians and astronomers, an astonishing natural coincidence helped to keep it alive among the educated public. The flare up of *supernovae* is an uncommon event in any galaxy. In the thousands of years of history only one had previously been recorded—that seen by the Chinese in 1054. Now two occurred within four decades. The earlier one began to flare in 1572 and for two years was the brightest object in the heavens. It was observed and described by Tycho Brahe, the Danish astronomer who was a meticulous recorder and a great improver of astronomical instruments. The second *supernova* appeared in equal brilliance in 1604, and so came to be recorded by Brahe's immediate successor, the German astronomer, Kepler. These extraordinary births in the immutable cosmos of the Aristotelians stimulated all thinking people to question the old assumptions more deeply.

Brahe attempted a compromise, suggesting that while the five planets might revolve round the sun, sun and planets together revolved round a stable earth. But Kepler out-thought his predecessor and succeeded in bringing the system of Copernicus to far greater perfection. There had been something appealing alike to simple and to subtle minds in the perfection of the circular orbit. Kepler broke away from it, finding from careful charting of the planet Mars that only elliptical orbits could explain the inconsistencies still remaining in the Copernican structure. So this astronomer demonstrated that the annual circum-solar journeys of the planets followed an ellipse, and that the plane of each orbit passed through the sun. He was also able to show that the rate of revolution of the planets round the sun varied in such proportion that 'the line from a planet to the sun sweeps out equal areas in equal intervals of time'.

Kepler cannot rank as a martyr of solar science for he was attacked more as a Protestant professor than for his Copernican heresies, and when he did at last have to leave the gymnasium at Gratz because under a Catholic regime pupils could no longer attend his classes, and he himself was not prepared to accept the rigid formula adopted by his academic superiors, it brought him nothing but advantage. He joined Brahe in his most up-to-date observatory near Prague just in time to inherit his position and all his data at the sudden death of the elder man.

The serious persecution began with Kepler's Italian contemporary, Galileo. This great man of the Renaissance, with typical versatility, on hearing of the invention of the two-lens telescope in Holland, had quickly deduced how to make his own, and had improved the design until he got a magnification of thirty-two. So now for the first time sun-regarding man was able greatly to increase the power of vision which evolution had allowed him. Among the many other astonishing things at once revealed to Galileo through his glass were the dark spots on the face of the sun, and by recording their apparent movement across the disk he was able to show that the sun, although it had now been anchored at the heart of the planetary system, nevertheless spun on its own axis.

Galileo exhibited his telescopes in Venice and Rome and at first was applauded by the Pope and his hierarchy. But fear, with its agent, censure, were being created. Several of the astronomer's colleagues at the University of Padua refused to look down the evil tube. What was seen through it was an illusion they said, the handiwork of the devil. So the devil, who had already invented false Eucharists in honour of the Sun God, was now busy putting spots on the solar countenance.

Much worse was to follow. From now on, excited and made confident by his wonderful discoveries, Galileo openly proclaimed the Copernican theory, even trying to justify it from the point of view of the scriptures. More and more clearly it was recognized as a dangerous theological issue, and the astronomer was soon contending with the Holy Office. When he went to Rome to explain his views, his ardour and eloquence only made matters worse. In 1616 the consulting theologians of the Inquisition took the two propositions 'that the sun is immovable in the centre of the world, and that the earth has a diurnal rotation' and declared the first to be 'absurd in philosophy and formally heretical, because expressly contrary to Holy Scripture' and the second as 'open to the same censure in philosophy and at least as erroneous as to faith'.

Immediately afterwards Cardinal Bellarmine (so greatly loathed in England) sent for him and gave him some kind of warning against teaching or defending the heretical theory. Much later, when Galileo was on trial, a document was produced to show that he had sworn to keep an absolute prohibition, but it is now thought that this may have been a forgery. Certainly he returned home reasonably well pleased with his treatment.

He kept silence for some time on the dangerous subject, but when a known admirer of his became Pope and he was everywhere assured that the Church looked on him with tolerance, he returned at least indirectly to the attack. He decided to expound his ideas under cover of an imaginary discussion. In his *Dialogue on the Two Principal World Systems* written between about 1625 and 1630, while his own views were ably put by one Salviati, the orthodox doctrine was defended by Simplicio, a plodding Aristotelian who was sometimes treated with contempt. The book is brilliantly written, and on its publication in 1632 was greeted with enthusiastic praise all over Europe. But it did not please the Holy Office, who rightly saw it as flouting the decree of 1616. Sale of the book was stopped, and Galileo, ageing and unwell, was called to Rome to stand trial before the Inquisition. His choice of the dialogue form proved most unfortunate, for not only was he accused of having disobeyed Bellarmine's directive, but the Pope, once his friend, fancied he was being mocked in the character of Simplicio.

The ailing scientist, one of the most distinguished minds in Europe, was threatened with torture. It is said that it was never intended that it should be used, but nevertheless this seems a strange way of establishing the truth of scripture. Galileo recanted, and read aloud a denial of all that he held to be true. So it was outwardly maintained for a little longer that the sun went round the earth. On the death of Galileo in 1642, the Pope insisted that no monument to him must bear words which could 'offend the reputation of the Holy Office'.

It is no chance that the next step towards the understanding of the workings of the solar system took place in Britain. The Roman Catholic Church had by now almost stifled astronomical heresy in Italy and parts of Germany; Luther, too, had nothing but contempt for Copernican ideas. Descartes in France had invented a cosmic scheme of his own which the Holy Office was prepared to let pass. He said that the world consisted of a number of vortices of ethereal 'primary matter' surrounding all solid bodies of whatever size, which attracted and repelled one another. The Inquisition had insisted that the earth did not move. Nor did it in his theory. The earth remained fixed in its small vortex, the sun in its large one and all that moved was the earth's vortex which went round the sun. This ingenious plea saved Descartes and many others from charges of heresy.

The England in which Newton was born was a revolutionary as well as a Protestant land. Although the Enlightenment had not yet begun, the Sun of Intellect was very much in the ascendant. Working on the planetary laws of Kepler and the discoveries concerning the mechanics of motion which were probably Galileo's best theoretical work, the extraordinary genius of the Englishman was able not only to envisage the gravitational system and devise the famous law that *the force of the sun acting upon the planets must vary as the inverse square of the distances of the planets from the sun*—several men had been speculating in this direction—but also to prove it exhaustively by experiment and calculation. With the publication about 1687 of the *Principia Mathematica* all the work which had been done by ancient Greeks and their European inheritors was brought into a smooth-working mechanical picture of the universe that was long to remain unchanged. The sun had come into its own in the secular world. Not only could it at last be proved beyond any resistance by the Holy Office that the earth and planets serenely orbited round its central fire, but also that they were supported in their journeys by its gravitational might.

It is pleasing that Newton, who played so gigantic a part in bringing mankind to a fuller understanding of the working of the solar system, should also, and in fact at an earlier date, have made great progress in interpreting the nature of light. Sunlight had created eyes, and eyes had done much to build and feed the brain, and now mind was to analyse this creative sunlight. Newton, who was skilful with 'glasses' of all kinds, both lenses and prisms, used them for intensive study of the solar spectrum. Before him men had supposed that the colours of the rainbow must be some secondary acquisites of light—once again it seemed against all 'appearances'—against common sense—that the everyday white light bathing the earth should itself contain all these intense and varied hues. Newton was able to satisfy himself and most of his fellow scientists that they did in truth compose white light, that they could be divided into the spectrum because they had different angles of refraction, and, moreover, 'that the colours of all natural bodies have no other origin than this, that they are variously qualified to reflect one sort of light in greater plenty than another'. So another secret between man and the sun was out: all the beautiful colours of the world were in light and the eye of the beholder. Beyond that Newton went wrong, for he decided to prefer the corpuscular to the wave theory of light, securing that this would hold the field for the next two and a half centuries. Nor, of course, could he possibly conceive the chemical origin of his variously 'Refrangible Rays', or guess that his successors would be able to read in the spectrum the very composition of the sun.

Sir Isaac Newton best represents the arrival of the modern world not only for the size and coherence of his discoveries, but for the methods he perfected. With a few exceptions the Greeks had avoided physical experiments, perhaps regarding them as banausic, and although earlier Renaissance workers had used them, it tended to be in an erratic fashion. Sir Francis Bacon has been acclaimed as the father of the inductive method, but beside Newton he was a dilettante. The physicist fully accepted the method in all its rigour—the repeated observation of the particular leading to the formulation of the theory, tested by still further repeated experiment. Here was the instrument which has given man his present terrifying power over the physical world.

Up to now most observers of the heavenly bodies, whether they were recording facts or making theories, whether they were interested for religious or for scientific reasons, had been primarily concerned with their movements. These had been most important both from a religious and a practical point of view for the making of calendars and the measurement of the seasons. They had also become more and more important for the astrology which all men, learned as well as ignorant, had accepted as an exact science.

Newton's gravitational laws made the calculation of orbits and other motions far more searching and precise, and soon stimulated an enormous amount of fresh work on the planetary system. All kinds of ingenious and beautiful instruments were devised for the purpose. These included models of the solar family intended for the enlightenment of the general public. Some kind of familiarity with such matters became part of the polite education of a gentleman—and even of a lady. Yet while the motions of heavenly bodies were more than ever enthusiastically studied, some interest was bound to shift to fresh problems—to the estimation of sizes, weights and distances, and to the composition and nature of the bodies themselves. Astronomy also turned towards more distant space, the penetrating power of the telescope soon shattering the crystal sphere of the fixed stars. But that is another story.

Aristarchus, it will be remembered, had made a brave attempt to estimate the relative distance of the sun and moon from the earth; to measure absolute distances proved difficult. Yet to get an exact figure for this basic astronomical unit was a pressing need. The first essays depended upon measurements of parallax. In 1672 astronomers in Paris and Cayenne made combined observations on the planet Mars which gave the earth's mean distance from the sun as eighty-seven million miles, a figure inaccurate by astronomical standards but close enough to the truth to make very little difference to most of us. Later efforts tended to concentrate on transits—the passage of the inner planets, Mercury and Venus, across the face of the sun. Transits of Venus were used in 1761 and 1769. Nineteenth-century estimates, based on much the same methods, gave ninety-one and ninety-five million miles, nearer to the correct figure though one was too small, the other too great.

Yet another method used depended upon the speed of light. Olaus Römer has a distinguished place in solar history for his brilliant proof that this speed could be measured—that it was, in fact, finite. This he did in 1675 through patient and ingenious observation of eclipses of Jupiter's moons. Just over two centuries later, when the actual velocity of light was known, Newcomb came very near to the correct answer with an estimate of ninety-three million miles. This figure, however, was still distrusted. During the 1930's a great international effort was made with observers all over the world using the minor planet Eros (which comes within fifteen million miles of the earth) as their point of reference. In 1941 the English Astronomer Royal, Spencer Jones, was able to announce to the listening earth that its average distance from the sun was 93,003,000 miles. Even while I have been writing the later chapters of this book, small corrections of distances within the solar system have been made possible by instruments fired clear of the earth's atmosphere.

Yet although perfectionists have continued to polish the figures, men's minds have now long comprehended the more important measurements of the solar system. For the best-informed Greeks it had been possible seriously to suggest that the sun was one foot in diameter, or that it was 'larger than the Peloponnese'. By the beginning of the nineteenth century the distances, dimensions, velocities and masses of the sun and most of its satellites were known with very reasonable accuracy.

It must be admitted that not quite all the dependants of the sun had been detected at this time. During thousands of years mankind had watched the Five Planets and often linked their movements with its own fate. Then in 1781 that indefatigable searcher of the skies, Sir William Herschel, added Uranus to the ancient Five. Uranus itself pointed the way to the next discovery. A minute discrepancy was found between the calculated and actual orbit of the new planet, and with calculations based on gravitation so fine that they should have made Newton sing in his grave, the position of some unknown source of attraction was estimated. In 1846 the bodily presence of Neptune was observed by telescope. Pluto was tracked down in 1930.

So now men had measured and numbered the ancient divinities of their sky. No longer fearful of impiety, they went on to the next analysis. What was the sun made of? Since Newton's pioneering work many studies of the solar spectrum had been made, and Herschel had suspected that invisible radiations also reached earth from the sun. The early nineteenth century was a great time for chemistry, and already the chemical basis of spectroscopic colours was being realized when in 1859–60 two German workers, Bunsen and Kirchoff, brought spectrum analysis to a new pitch and showed how it could be used to discover the exact composition of the sun and stars. So now the ingredients in the solar recipe could be read off from

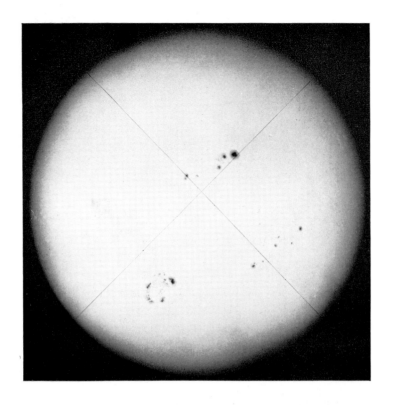

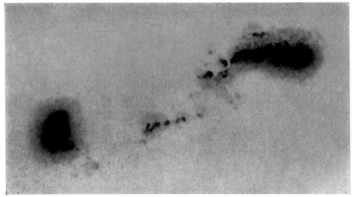

IX. (*a*) The Sun photographed in white light, showing groups of sunspots

(*b*) 'Close-up' of a group of sunspots

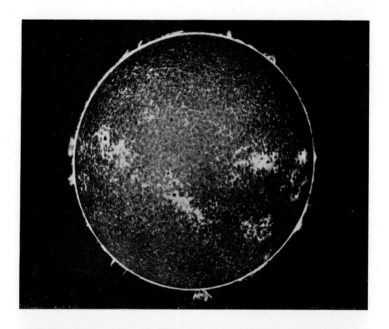

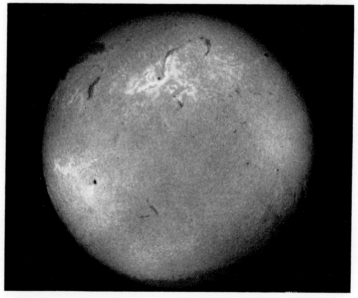

X. (a) The Sun photographed along calcium wavelength
(b) The Sun photographed along hydrogen wavelength

the pretty colours and dark lines marshalled by the prism, and it was soon realized that chemically the body of Sol was almost identical with that of our cold and solid earth. That the sun was our parent appeared more than ever likely.

Side by side with the later developments of spectrum analysis went the improvement of photographic portraiture of the sun. The disk has been drawn with human features for so long that men will always think of the 'face' of the sun. But now the spectrohelioscope was to catch a more scientific likeness. By taking photographs on selected wavelengths of the spectrum, it has become possible to portray the star with many different complexions according to the element represented. Thus there can be a calcium likeness, a hydrogen likeness and so forth—each with its own distinctive character. Moreover, further ingenuity has enabled cinematographic pictures to be taken of the sun's atmosphere. Filmed in the hydrogen-red wavelength, the tumultuous scenes staged there are as beautiful as they are dramatic. Indeed, films speeded up several hundred times to show the great incandescent arches and fountains leaping from the star, are among the most awe-inspiring spectacles ever revealed by science.

In the past astronomers of all nations streamed from continent to continent following the shadow of the moon—to observe the sun's atmosphere at the instant of total eclipse. Ordinary interested mortals followed in their wake, until there were pilgrimages as large as those going to the shrine of the Sun Goddess at Ise. Now many of the phenomena can be better observed through the eye of the camera.

Today the sun is studied in almost as many observatories as it was once worshipped in temples. A number are now equipped with solar towers like those at Potsdam and Mount Wilson. Since 1942, when radar operators in Britain first picked up radio waves from the sun, radio telescopes have explored longwave radiations. They may be huge parabolic reflectors as at Jodrell Bank or lines of carefully spaced aerials. All round the world astronomers watch the sun day round and year long. Synoptic maps of the photosphere are issued from Zürich, of the chromosphere from Paris; daily maps come from German Freiburg. Our star is watched as closely as a dying king.

For scientific purposes great mirrors are used to concentrate the sun's heat to a point where thick metal sheets can be burnt like paper. Solar heat is also being harnessed for practical uses, ranging in scale from the amazing Soviet power station at Ararat in Armenia to the little one-woman sun cookers which Unesco has been spreading in India and other lands where fuel and power are still precious. A lighthouse has just been built with photo-electric cells to provide the illumination; many of the space vehicles which we are sending out to explore the solar system are also powered by photo-electric cells. This direct utilization of the sun's radiations will increase from year to year—though it is never likely to equal that quietly carried on by the vegetable world.

The study and utilization of our sun are now going on at such a pace that I cannot possibly do more than point in their direction. Anyone who wants to know more need only read the daily press, the magazines and paperbacks. Scientific discovery has generated such a state of intellectual light as to be bewildering. And while it is obvious that the boundaries between different sciences are rapidly breaking down to produce a single account of the physical universe (in which sun and man merge into one another and into the totality of energy and matter), the highly specialized scientists themselves are less and less able to communicate either with one another or with the rest of us.

In the face of all that I must leave out, there is one other region of thought I want to recall before entering the final phase of this narrative. Our intellectual searchlights have swivelled from point to point of the outside world; last of all we have attempted to turn a beam inward upon the hitherto secret and sacred depths of our own minds. There, as I hope all readers of this book will have come to expect, psychologists have found potent and crowding solar images. From dreams, poems and drawings have emerged innumerable figures of day and night, light and darkness, with their train of moral and spiritual meanings. Rising above them all have been the images of Sol himself, always standing for the emergent ego, the full sun of individual consciousness.

Now I enter upon the last phase of man's relationship with the sun. That of imitation. It will, I hope, precisely complete the solar cycle I have attempted to draw—from the sun making man round and back to man making suns. It is a phase short and appallingly tragic.

I have not yet mentioned the time aspect of solar science, for the reason that curiously enough it introduces these closing events. After Darwin, estimates of the antiquity of the solar system began to be made—which is not surprising as more even than it was an age of science, the nineteenth century was an age of history. One set of estimates was drawn up by the geologists from their reading of the rocks. They saw the colossal scale of evolutionary change and demanded thousands of millions of years to contain it. The astronomers and physicists, on the other hand, led by Lord Kelvin, produced what they considered irrefutable arguments to prove that the solar system could not be more than a few hundred million years old at most. One of their arguments concerned the duration of the cooling of the earth, which was then supposed certainly to have started in a molten state. Another, based on the law of the conservation of energy, involved the length of time for which the sun could have continued to pour out its heat and light without some kind of refuelling. Kelvin estimated that the sun might have maintained its present output for about one hundred million years. Five hundred million he declared to be out of the question.

The geologists, while conducting a vigorous controversy, continued in pursuit of their ideas. No doubt the physicists, with their long tradition and overwhelming mathematical knowledge, considered them brash and unscientific. Yet the upstarts of the young science were right, for the usual reason that there were more things in heaven and earth than even the most brilliant physicists had dreamed of. There was radio-activity.

This essential yet hitherto unsuspected factor in our universe first began to come to human notice during the last decade of the nineteenth century. The earliest assaults on the atom were mild-seeming enough. Electric charges run through gas some-times produced a ghostly blue-green light flickering on the glass walls of the tube as though a will-o'-the-wisp were im-prisoned there. Soon this phenomenon was connected with the comparable natural fluorescence of certain substances such as uranium. Owing to the almost demonic brilliance and energy of Pierre and Marie Curie, radium, the most powerful of all natural sources of radioactivity, as they named it, was isolated by 1902.

Already by this year Rutherford had realized that natural radioactivity was due to the breakdown of atoms and their metamorphosis into others quite different. The belief that the atom was the smallest particle of matter, eternally irreducible, had been disproved, while the transmutation of elements, the alchemists' dream, had been shown to take place even without man's assistance. Needless to say, from that moment there were plenty of men determined to assist.

Radioactivity was at once seen as a likely explanation of the long life of the sun already insisted upon by the geologists. At first it was thought that the existence in the sun of the same radioactive substances that were being found on earth might be enough to provide the necessary sources of energy. But it was not long before this was seen to be impossible. The tremendous heat and pressure within the star must be releasing other forms of atomic power.

Sir Arthur Eddington is another hero of solar research. During the first quarter of our own century, using the stream of discoveries then being made by Rutherford and many others, he carried out a mental probe reaching to the very heart of the sun. In popularizing his work he wrote, 'We can now form some kind of picture of the inside of a star—a hurly burly of atoms, electrons and ether waves. The stately drama of stellar evolution turns out to be more like the hair-breadth escapades of the films. The music of the spheres has almost a suggestion— of jazz.' The mind of man was thrusting into the once worshipful body of the sun. But this was still the innocent age.

The light of the Apollonian mind which, having revealed the form, motions, dimensions and ingredients of the sun, was now about to show how its inmost being, the ancient power of the Sun God, could be imitated by man on earth, had always depended first on analysis—on processes of breaking down. This in contrast with art and religion, which have always been devoted to creating larger unities. It is therefore perfectly appropriate that the brain was now at last to be focused upon the final annihilation of matter. If it was also to cause the annihilation of itself and all other forms of life, that, too, could be called appropriate.

Until this time the physicists had only been playing with the electrons which orbit about the nucleus of each atom in a manner which has often, but not I think very illuminatingly, been likened to the solar system. Now the time had come to break down the central nucleus in which such tremendous energy lay clasped. As the points where the Apollonian minds of physicists shone most brightly flashed between Cambridge, Göttingen, Copenhagen, Rome and Berlin, the onslaught was maintained, the atomic nuclei of various elements being hammered with ever more powerful electric charges. This went on without success for many years, yet in fact the means of fission had lain to hand since Chadwick discovered the neutron in 1932. The neutron, because it was electrically negative, could steal into the nucleus without opposition, and indeed had been doing so unperceived in many experiments with uranium during the period of apparent unsuccess. It was at the very end of 1938 that Hahn, Lise Meitner and her nephew Frisch demonstrated that neutrons were dividing the nucleus of uranium into two slightly unequal parts—into the nuclei, that is to say, of other elements.

The dreadful story of the next five years is not a proper part of this chronicle, for the fission bomb was not based on solar principles. It is only necessary to say that now for the first time physics, which had done so much to expose the secrets of the Sun God, was to be deeply involved in that fearful survival from man's past: warfare. Already one chosen people, the Germans, had expelled another chosen people, the Jews, and very many of those expelled were involved in the deadly researches. Unhappily, no sooner were they on the other side of the Atlantic than they became caught up in the world of 'we' versus 'they', which is to say of day against night, good against evil. Although perhaps no previous war came nearer to justifying the primitive notion of children of light contending against children of darkness, man's hope of salvation lay in the scientists refusing to share in it. Yet the physicists of the Allies built the bomb for their military because they were afraid that otherwise 'they' would do so first. Looking back on that history now, their efforts to prevent the use of the evil thing they had created seem puerile. How could they have believed it would not be used as soon as it was complete?

They cannot be excused, but they can be forgiven for their colossal error. It is harder to forgive those of them who fell into error a second time in identically the same way. The only difference is that in the interval a political nuclear fission has taken place: 'we' now includes the Germans; the Russians have split off and become 'they'.

This time the story does belong in my chronicle, indeed forms its inevitable ending, for the processes of the H-bomb are those of the sun.

In the 'Twenties Göttingen was the centre of a galaxy of

brilliant young physicists. (It seems almost as though a few exceptional brains have some innate knowledge of the processes behind their own creation which becomes clouded and obscured with thought and experience. For almost all mathematical brains of this kind do their best work before their owners are thirty years old.) In the summer of 1927 two of these young men went on a walking tour. One was the Englishman Atkinson, fresh from Rutherford's Cavendish laboratory, the other was the German, Houtermans, who afterwards helped to prevent an A-bomb being placed in Hitler's hands.

It is said that as they walked through the warm sunshine they began once more to discuss the old problem of the source of so much light and heat. For although Eddington had gone far, they knew that the answer had not yet been found. Atkinson suggested that it must lie in some such transmutation of the elements as he had witnessed at the Cavendish. Houtermans agreed, and they resolved to work it out. This was the beginning of their theory that the sun was stoked not by an atomic fission but by the fusion of lightweight atoms, in fact by the fusion of hydrogen into helium which was subsequently proved. Houtermans has recorded how, after he had finished a definitive essay on the subject, 'I went for a walk with a pretty girl. As soon as it grew dark the stars came out in all their splendour. "Don't they sparkle beautifully?" cried my companion. But I simply stuck out my chest and said proudly: "I've known since yesterday why it is that they sparkle." She didn't seem in the least moved by this statement. . . . At that moment, probably, she felt no interest whatever in the matter.' Yet he was referring to the ideas and calculations which were to lead directly to the manufacture of the H-bomb. This reply, so full of hubris, which Houtermans made instead of agreeing with the girl and kissing her, seems to me well to represent one of the dangerous faults of the Apollonian mind.

Already during wartime when his colleagues were still perfecting the fission bomb, Edward Teller was working on the theory of a weapon which would exploit the vastly greater violence of atomic fusion. By the time the very genuine efforts of many scientists in America to establish international control of atomic weapons had failed and the Russians had exploded their own bomb, it began to be suggested that if what was now 'the West', the children of light, were to survive then this new version of the final weapon must be made. 'Such a bomb could only be constructed if the powerful natural processes taking place in the interior of the sun were to be successfully reproduced on earth.'

At the end of this book, before the Hymn to the Sun of Akhenaten and the Prayer of the Emperor Julian, I have reproduced the formula underlying the solar process and the H-bomb—the formula of life and of death.

Edward Teller had been a refugee from anti-Semitism in Hungary, and then again from Nazi Germany. His grim experience had filled him, evidently, with an implacable hatred of what he would call totalitarianism, but which might perhaps better be called 'enemies' in general. The Sun of Intellect in him shone clearly enough to make him ask for World Government as the only means to peace, but at the same time he threw all his real strength into the creation of his diabolical weapon. One is reminded of the unhappy Aztec priests who were sure of being 'merciful and compassionate' even while they tore out living hearts.

I think it fair to say that this man more than any other was responsible for overcoming the guilty consciences of a sufficient number of his fellow countrymen to enable the project to go forward. He was, of course, continuously assisted by the Russians who were equally convinced that 'they', the Americans, were planning to destroy them. After the respite of 1949 when it seemed as though saner men were about to prevail, the Fuchs case made the Russians appear even blacker and longer-horned than before.

On 31st January 1950 President Truman, using language

appropriately dead, made this announcement. 'I have directed the Atomic Energy Commission to continue its work on all forms of atomic weapons, including the so-called hydrogen or super-bomb. Like all other work in the field of atomic weapons, it is being and will be carried forward on a basis consistent with the overall objectives of our programme for peace and security.' Helped by that parasite of the Apollonian mind, an electronic computer, the work went forward with deadly speed.

During the autumn of 1952 thousands of scientists, engineers and nuclear warriors congregated at the coral island of Eniwetok in the Marshall Islands. The bomb-makers, with their sickening fondness for trivializing high tragedy, called their creation Mike. We can, I suppose, be thankful that the P.R. men had not been allowed to name it New Hope or Peace Maker. The thing was set up on the islet of Elugaleb. When it was detonated on the morning of 1st November, a fireball three and a half miles across lifted into the air and Elugaleb disappeared below the sea. Five thousand miles away the anxious father, Edward Teller, watching a seismograph at Berkeley, California, saw the indicator dance wildly. He was not sure whether his hand shook.

Man's first artificial sun rose above the Pacific, but it was not a star of peace. The Russians watched their own sun rise within a year. So now two chosen people, each confident that they were the children of light, confronted one another across the globe with suns in their bandoliers.

Before the decade was out earth had its man-made satellites and the face of the moon had been struck. In this present year of A.D. 1962, three representatives of *Homo sapiens* have already seen the sun shining in the black skies of interplanetary space. The pace quickens.

Prometheus stole fire from the gods, the fire which has so often been kindled as a symbol of the sun. We have stolen the secret formula of the sun itself. The Titan defied Almighty Zeus on behalf of mankind, and for his sacrilege had to suffer torments from the talons of the eagle, bird of the sun. So he has been a hero for all Apollonians, for the Greeks, for the men of the Renaissance, for ourselves. Prometheus, yes, and Icarus, Phaeton and Faust as well. Is our modern Prometheus, the total scientist, in his greater pride, his more reckless defiance of the gods, about to lead us all to self-destruction? In our hundreds of millions we mass on the face of the earth in helpless expectation of a searing death more terrible than that spread by Phaeton when he found he could not hold the horses of the sun.

In following the solar cycle of this book, I have honoured those who worshipped the Sun God in his many forms. Yet I have also honoured those scientists whose probing minds have dispelled the simple divinity of the star. The members of the Holy Office were right to be fearful of the ideas of Copernicus, to see that they would lead to the destruction of many of the old religious forms. They were wrong as well as ridiculous in trying to turn back the tide of science, of man's efforts to comprehend the physical universe, for that pursuit is a part of what is divine in humanity. We have to honour both the King of Heaven and Prometheus.

The present peril and despair of humanity show that we cannot live without religious meaning although we may well do without religious institutions. (The time may come when even those few who still follow them turn against priests who, in gem-encrusted copes and mitres, serve Him who taught poverty and humility, who betray Him who taught love of one's enemy by raising no murmur against a holocaust of hate.) If we cannot find god in the world, we lose Him in ourselves and become contemptible in our own eyes. We become mere statistics. For this is the greatest evil coming from the unbalanced Apollonian mind. Science has won power over the universe of matter by breaking down and down, by numbering and measuring. So at last everything that cannot be broken down, numbered and measured must be deemed not to exist. Science is uniting man with the sun in a totality of energy and matter. That is communion at the lowest level of being. But we have always been right to seek it also at the highest.

The Sun of Intellect shining fierce and alone overhead will make the whole globe a Golgotha. Forms of religious expression, like art, are means towards harmonizing the dark and light within each one of us—those terrible forces, potent as the atom, that are driving us to destruction. We have to find this means of letting light into the dark places, and darkness to temper the light. The late Roman Empire gave birth to Christianity. Will our own world, which so poignantly resembles it, have life and strength for another labour?

It seems that a new religion must exalt the Sun of Life more successfully than Christianity has ever succeeded in doing. It is some proof of our need that the man who has proclaimed 'a reverence for life' as his creed has come to be accepted as a saint of the modern world. The morality of the new religion cannot be of the prohibitive, life-denying kind which may, alas, only serve to strengthen the inner forces of darkness, our sense of 'the enemy', but a no less strenuous positive morality directed towards creative love in all its manifestations. It must respect the chicken crying for life within the shell equally with the light of thought within the skull. Akhenaten in his gardens by the Nile had a vision of what might be, but it was too soon. If we cannot move nearer to this vision now, it will be too late.

I have a hesitant conviction that the young are already moving towards these new forms, infected though they are with our own corruption. I often look at them with distaste and with a great hope. They are stripped down to bare bones of truth and acceptance which could soon be reclothed from head to foot. Many of the attitudes which the older generations delight in censuring (because, like the Inquisition, we are afraid) may well mark stumbling advances towards a better morality.

Meanwhile the sun shines upon us all in turn, the black and the white, the peoples of the East and the peoples of the West. There is just a chance that it may awaken us to a Good Morning.

GERMANIC SUN-IDOL
From the *Sachsisch Chronicon*, 1596

APPENDICES

SUN FORMULA

The Processes Continually Maintained Inside the Sun

$$H^1 (p, \beta) H^2 \qquad \text{(i)}$$
$$H^2 (p, \gamma) He^3 \qquad \text{(ii)}$$
$$He^3 (He^3, 2p) He^4 \qquad \text{(iii)}$$

In reaction (i) H^1 is hydrogen, ordinary hydrogen with a nucleus containing one particle, a proton. The H symbol in H^2 signifies hydrogen, and the 2 signifies a nucleus with two particles. Since the chemical element hydrogen has 1 proton this implies a nucleus with 1 proton and 1 neutron. Such a nucleus is known, and is called the deuteron. The symbolism of reaction (i) tells us that a proton added to H^1 makes H^2—a proton plus a proton makes a nucleus with 1 proton and 1 neutron. This requires a proton to change into a neutron during the process and this is indicated by the symbol β. Reaction (ii) implies that a proton added to H^2 (1 proton, 1 neutron) gives the isotope He^3 (2 protons, 1 neutron) of helium, radiation being emitted in the reaction. Reaction (iii) implies that He^3 (2 protons, 1 neutron), when added to He^3 (2 protons, 1 neutron), gives the isotope He^4 (2 protons, 2 neutrons) of helium and that 2 protons are ejected in the reaction.

The net effect of the three reactions is that hydrogen is converted to helium. Energy appears as an electron of positive character (positron) emitted in the β process of reaction (i), in the radiation emitted in (ii), and in the energy of motion of the two protons that are ejected in reaction (iii). These add their energy to the material of the star. A neutrino emitted in the β process carries its energy away from the star, however, and this is irretrievably lost.

THE PHARAOH AKHENATEN'S HYMN TO THE SUN

A   You rise glorious at the heavens' edge, O living Aten!
You in whom all life began.
When you shone from the eastern horizon
You filled every land with your beauty.
You are lovely, great and glittering,
You go high above the lands you have made,
Embracing them with your rays,
Holding them fast for your beloved son.[1]
Though you are far away, your rays are on earth;
Though you fill men's eyes, your footprints are unseen.

B   When you sink beyond the western boundary of the
      heavens
The earth is darkened as though by death;
Then men sleep in their bedchambers,
Their heads wrapped up, unable to see one another;
Their treasures are stolen from beneath their heads
And they know it not.
Every lion comes out from his lair,
All serpents emerge and sting.
Darkness is supreme and the earth silent;
Their maker rests within his horizon.

[1] Akhenaten.

C   The earth brightens with your rising,
    With the shining of your disk by day;
    Before your rays the darkness is put to flight.
    The people of the Two Lands celebrate the day,
    You rouse them and raise them to their feet,
    They wash their limbs, they dress themselves,
    They lift up their arms in praise of your appearing,
    Then through all the land they begin their work.

D   Cattle browse peacefully,
    Trees and plants are verdant,
    Birds fly from their nests
    And lift up their wings in your praise.
    All animals frisk upon their feet
    All winged things fly and alight once more—
    They come to life with your rising.

E   Boats sail upstream and boats sail downstream,
    At your coming every highway is opened.
    Before your face the fish leap up from the river,
    Your rays reach the green ocean.
    You it is who place the male seed in woman,
    Who create the semen in man;
    You quicken the son in his mother's belly,
    Soothing him so that he shall not cry.
    Even in the womb you are his nurse.
    You give breath to all your creation,
    Opening the mouth of the newborn
    And giving him nourishment.

F   When the chicken chirps from within the shell
    You give him breath that he may live.
    You bring his body to readiness
    So that he may break from the egg.
    And when he is hatched he runs on his two feet
    Announcing his creation.

248

G   How manifold are your works!
    They are mysterious in men's sight.
    O sole, incomparable god, all powerful,
    You created the earth in solitude
    As your heart desired.
    Men you created, and cattle great and small,
    Whatever is on earth,
    All that tread the ground on foot,
    All that wing the lofty air.
    You created the strange countries, Khor and Kush
    As well as the Land of Egypt.
    You set every man in his right place
    With his food and his possessions
    And his days that are numbered.
    Men speak in many tongues,
    In body and complexion they are various,
    For you have distinguished between people and people.

H   In the Netherworld you make the Nile-flood
    Leading it out at your pleasure to bring life for the
        Egyptians.
    Though lord of them all, lord of their lands,
    You grow weary for them, shine for them,
    The Sun Disk by day, great in your majesty.
    To far lands also you have brought life,
    Setting them a Nile-flood in the heavens
    That falls like the waves of the sea
    Watering the fields where they dwell.

I   How excellent are your purposes, O lord of eternity!
    You have set a Nile in the sky for the strangers,
    For the cattle of every country that go on their feet.
    But for Egypt the Nile wells from the Netherworld.
    Your rays nourish field and garden
    It is for you that they live.

J   You make the seasons for the sake of your creation,
The winter to cool them, the summer that they may
    taste your heat.
You have made far skies so that you may shine in them,
Your disk in its solitude looks on all that you have made,
Appearing in its glory and gleaming both near and far.
Out of your singleness you shape a million forms—
Towns and villages, fields, roads and the river.
All eyes behold you, bright Disk of the day.

K   There is none other who knows you save Akhenaten,[1]
    your son,
You have given him insight of your purposes
He understands your power.
All the creatures of the world are in your hand
Just as you have made them.
With your rising they live, with your setting they die.
You yourself are the span of life, men live through you
Their eyes filled with beauty till the hour of your setting.
All labour is set aside
When you sink in the west.

L   You established the world for your son,
He who was born of your body,
King of Upper Egypt and Lower Egypt,
Living in Truth, Lord of the Two Lands,
Neferkheprure, Wanre
The Son of Re, Living in Truth, Lord of Diadems,
Akhenaten great in his length of days.
And for the King's Great Wife,
She whom he loves,
For the Lady of the Two Lands, Nefernefruaten-
    Nefertiti
May she live and flower for ever and ever.

[1] The actual title used in this line is Neferkheprure.

SELECTION FROM THE EMPEROR JULIAN'S
HYMN TO KING HELIOS

[These passages represent rather less than a half of the Hymn, which is Oration IV in the works of the Emperor. They are taken from the Loeb edition, translated and annotated by W. C. Wright.]

What I am now about to say I consider to be of the greatest importance for all things 'That breathe and move upon the earth', and have a share in existence and a reasoning soul and intelligence, but above all others it is of importance to myself. For I am a follower of King Helios. And of this fact I possess within me, known to myself alone, proofs more certain than I can give.[1] But this at least I am permitted to say without sacrilege, that from my childhood an extraordinary longing for the rays of the god penetrated deep into my soul; and from my earliest years my mind was so completely swayed by the light that illumines the heavens that not only did I desire to gaze intently at the sun, but whenever I walked abroad in the night season, when the firmament was clear and cloudless, I abandoned all else without exception and gave myself up to the beauties of the heavens; nor did I understand what anyone might say to me, nor heed what I was doing myself. I was considered to be over-curious about these matters and to pay

[1] He refers to his initiation into the cult of Mithras.

too much attention to them, and people went so far as to regard me as an astrologer when my beard had only just begun to grow.

Now for my part I envy the good fortune of any man to whom the god has granted to inherit a body built of the seed of holy and inspired ancestors, so that he can unlock the treasures of wisdom; nor do I despise that lot with which I was myself endowed by the god Helios, that I should be born of a house that rules and governs the world in my time; but further, I regard this god, if we may believe the wise, as the common father of all mankind. For it is said with truth that man and the sun together beget man, and that the god sows this earth with souls which proceed not from himself alone but from the other gods also; and for what purpose, the souls reveal by the kind of lives that they select. Now far the best thing is when anyone has the fortune to have inherited the service of the god, even before the third generation, from a long and unbroken line of ancestors; yet it is not a thing to be disparaged when anyone, recognizing that he is by nature intended to be the servant of Helios, either alone of all men, or in company with but few, devotes himself to the service of his master.

Come then, let me celebrate, as best I may, his festival which the Imperial city adorns with annual sacrifices.[1] Now it is hard, as I well know, merely to comprehend how great is the Invisible, if one judge by his visible self,[2] and to tell it is perhaps impossible, even though one should consent to fall short of what is his due. For well I know that no one in the world could attain to a description that would be worthy of him, and not to fail of a certain measure of success in his praises is the greatest height to which human beings can attain in the power of

[1] The festival was celebrated in Rome at the beginning of January.
[2] Julian distinguishes the visible sun from his archetype, the offspring of the Good.

utterance. But as for me, may Hermes, the god of eloquence, stand by my side to aid me, and the Muses also and Apollo, the leader of the Muses, since he too has oratory for his province, and may they grant that I utter only what the gods approve that men should say and believe about them. What, then, shall be the manner of my praise? Or is it not evident that if I describe his substance and his origin, and his powers and energies, both visible and invisible, and the gift of blessings which he bestows throughout all the worlds,[1] I shall compose an encomium not wholly displeasing to the god? With these, then, let me begin.

This divine and wholly beautiful universe, from the highest vault of heaven to the lowest limit of the earth, is held together by the continuous providence of the god, has existed from eternity ungenerated, is imperishable for all time to come, and is guarded immediately by nothing else than the Fifth Substance[2] whose culmination is the beams of the sun; and in the second and higher degree, so to speak, by the intelligible world; but in a still loftier sense it is guarded by the King of the whole universe, who is the centre of all things that exist. He, therefore, whether it is right to call him the Supra-Intelligible, or the Idea of Being, and by Being I mean the whole intelligible region, or the One, since the One seems somehow to be prior to all the rest, or, to use Plato's name for him, the Good; at any rate this uncompounded cause of the whole reveals to all existence beauty, and perfection, and oneness, and irresistible power; and in virtue of the primal creative substance that abides in it, produced, as middle among the middle and intellectual, creative causes, Helios the most mighty god, proceeding from itself and in all things like unto itself. Even so the divine Plato believed, when he writes, 'Therefore (said I) when I spoke of this, understand that I meant the offspring of the Good which the

---

[1] I.e. the intelligible world, comprehended only by pure reason; the intellectual, endowed with intelligence; and thirdly the world of sense-perception.

[2] 'Aether', which Iamblichus called the Fifth Element.

Good begat in his own likeness, and that what the Good is in relation to pure reason and its objects in the intelligible world, such is the sun in the visible world in relation to sight and its objects.' Accordingly his light has the same relation to the visible world as truth has to the intelligible world. And he himself as a whole, since he is the son of what is first and greatest, namely, the Idea of the Good, and subsists from eternity in the region of its abiding substance, has received also the dominion among the intellectual gods, and himself dispenses to the intellectual gods those things of which the Good is the cause for the intelligible gods. Now the Good is, I suppose, the cause for the intelligible gods of beauty, existence, perfection, and oneness, connecting these and illuminating them with a power that works for good. These accordingly Helios bestows on the intellectual gods also, since he has been appointed by the Good to rule and govern them, even though they came forth and came into being together with him, and this was, I suppose, in order that the cause which resembles the Good may guide the intellectual gods to blessings for them all, and may regulate all things according to pure reason.

But this visible disc also, third[1] in rank, is clearly for the objects of sense-perception the cause of preservation, and this visible Helios is the cause for the visible gods[2] of just as many blessings as we said mighty Helios bestows on the intellectual gods.

Is not light itself a sort of incorporeal and divine form of the transparent in a state of activity?

And light is a form of this substance [the transparent], so to speak, which is the substratum of and coextensive with the heavenly bodies. And of light, itself incorporeal, the culmina-

---

[1] Julian conceives of the sun in three ways; first as transcendental, in which form he is indistinguishable from the Good in the intelligible world, secondly as Helios-Mithras, ruler of the intellectual gods, thirdly as the visible sun.

[2] The stars.

tion and flower, to so speak, is the sun's rays. Now the doctrine of the Phoenicians, who were wise and learned in sacred lore, declared that the rays of light everywhere diffused are the undefiled incarnation of pure mind. And in harmony with this is our theory, seeing that light itself is incorporeal, if one should regard its fountain-head, not as corporeal, but as the undefiled activity of mind pouring light into its own abode: and this is assigned to the middle of the whole firmament, whence it sheds its rays and fills the heavenly spheres with vigour of every kind and illumines all things with light divine and undefiled.

What power in the universe has this god when he rises and sets? Night and day he creates, and before our eyes changes and sways the universe. But to which of the other heavenly bodies does this power belong? How then can we now fail to believe, in view of this, in respect also to things more divine that the invisible and divine tribes of intellectual gods above the heavens are filled with power that works for good by him, even by him to whom the whole band of the heavenly bodies yields place, and whom all generated things follow, piloted by his providence? For that the planets dance about him as their king, in certain intervals, fixed in relation to him, and revolve in a circle with perfect accord, making certain halts, and pursuing to and fro their orbit, as those who are learned in the study of the spheres call their visible motions; and that the light of the moon waxes and wanes varying in proportion to its distance from the sun, is, I think, clear to all. Then is it not natural that we should suppose that the more venerable ordering of bodies among the intellectual gods corresponds to this arrangement?

Let us therefore comprehend, out of all his functions, first his power to perfect, from the fact that he makes visible the objects of sight in the universe, for through his light he perfects them; secondly, his creative and generative power from the changes wrought by him in the universe; thirdly, his power to link together all things into one whole, from the harmony of his motions towards one and the same goal; fourthly, his middle station we can comprehend from himself, who is midmost; and fifthly, the fact that he is established as king among the intellectual gods, from his middle station among the planets. Now if we see that these powers, or powers of similar importance, belong to any one of the other visible deities, let us not assign to Helios leadership among the gods. But if he has nothing in common with those other gods except his beneficent energy, and of this too he gives them all a share, then let us call to witness the priests of Cyprus who set up common altars to Helios and Zeus; but even before them let us summon as witness Apollo, who sits in council with our god. For this god declares: 'Zeus, Hades, Helios Serapis, three gods in one godhead!' Let us then assume that, among the intellectual gods, Helios and Zeus have a joint or rather a single sovereignty.

[Julian here emphasizes and explains the 'middleness' of Helios. He sees him not as the 'mean' but as a link between two extremes—a Mediator. Helios is midway between 'the visible gods who surround the universe and the immaterial and invisible gods who surround the Good'. The middleness of the sun seems to have been a Persian doctrine: Plutarch says, 'The principle of good most nearly resembles light, and the principle of evil darkness, and between both is Mithras; therefore the Persians call Mithras the Mediator.' Julian may also have had in mind the similarity between the sun as mediator and the Christian *Logos*.]

This then we must declare, that King Helios is One and proceeds from one god, even from the intelligible world which is itself One; and that he is midmost of the intellectual gods, stationed in their midst by every kind of mediateness that is harmonious and friendly, and that joins what is sundered; and that he brings together into one the last and the first, having in his own person the means of completeness, of connection, of generative life and of uniform being: and that for the world which we can perceive he initiates blessings of all sorts, not only by means of the light with which he illumines it, adorning it and giving it its splendour, but also because he calls into existence, along with himself, the substance of the Sun's angels; and that finally in himself he comprehends the ungenerated cause of things generated, and further, and prior to this, the ageless and abiding cause of the life of the imperishable bodies.[1]

The creative power of Zeus also coincides with him, by reason of which in Cyprus, as I said earlier, shrines are founded and assigned to them in common. And Apollo himself also we called to witness to our statements, since it is certainly likely that he knows better than we about his own nature. For he too abides with Helios and is his colleague by reason of the singleness of his thoughts and the stability of his substance and the consistency of his activity.

But Apollo too in no case appears to separate the departmental creative function of Dionysus from Helios. And since he always subordinates it to Helios and so indicates that Dionysus[2] is his partner on the throne, Apollo is the interpreter for us of the fairest purposes that are to be found with our god. Further Helios, since he comprehends in himself all the principles of the fairest intellectual synthesis, is himself Apollo the leader of the Muses. And since he fills the whole of our life with fair order, he begat Asclepios in the world, though even before the beginning of the world he had him by his side.

But though one should survey many other powers that belong to this god, never could one investigate them all. It is enough to have observed the following: That there is an equal and identical dominion of Helios and Zeus over the separate creation which is prior to substances, in the region, that is to

[1] The heavenly bodies.
[2] Julian calls Dionysus the son of Helios and the son of Zeus.

say, of the absolute causes which, separated from visible creation, existed prior to it; secondly we observed the singleness of
his thoughts which is bound up with the imperishableness and
abiding sameness that he shares with Apollo; thirdly, the
departmental part of his creative function which he shares with
Dionysus who controls divided substance; fourthly we have
observed the power of the leader of the Muses, revealed in
fairest symmetry and blending of the intellectual; finally we
comprehended that Helios, with Asclepios, fulfils the fair order
of the whole of life.

He assigned as his own station the mid-heavens, in order that
from all sides he may bestow equal blessings on the gods who
came forth by his agency and in company with him; and that
he may guide the seven spheres[1] in the heavens and the eighth
sphere also, yes and as I believe the ninth creation too, namely
our world which revolves for ever in a continuous cycle of
birth and death. For it is evident that the planets, as they dance
in a circle about him, preserve as the measure of their motion a
harmony between this god and their own movements; and that
the whole heaven also, which adapts itself to him in all its parts,
is full of gods who proceed from Helios.

Why should I go on to speak to you of Horus and of the
other names of gods, which all belong to Helios? For from his
works men have learned to know this god, who makes the
whole heavens perfect through the gift of intellectual blessings,
and gives it a share of intelligible beauty; and taking the heavens
as their starting-point, they have learned to know him both as a
whole and his parts also, from his abundant bestowal of good
gifts. For he exercises control over all movement, even to the
lowest plane of the universe. And everywhere he makes all
things perfect, nature and soul and everything that exists. And
marshalling together this great army of the gods into a single

[1] The seven planets; Helios is counted with them.

commanding unity, he handed it over to Athene Pronoia who, as the legend says, sprang from the head of Zeus, but I say that she was sent forth from Helios whole from the whole of him, being contained within him; though I disagree with the legend only so far as I assert that she came forth not from his highest part, but whole from the whole of him. For in other respects, since I believe that Zeus is in no wise different from Helios, I agree with that ancient tradition. And in using this very phrase Athene Pronoia, I am not innovating, if I rightly understand the words: 'He came to Pytho and to grey-eyed Pronoia.' This proves that the ancients also thought that Athene Pronoia shared the throne of Apollo, who, as we believe, differs in no way from Helios. Indeed, did not Homer by divine inspiration —for he was, we may suppose, possessed by a god—reveal this truth, when he says often in his poems: 'May I be honoured even as Athene and Apollo were honoured'—by Zeus, that is to say, who is identical with Helios? And just as King Apollo, through the singleness of his thoughts, is associated with Helios, so also we must believe that Athene has received her nature from Helios, and that she is his intelligence in perfect form: and so she binds together the gods who are assembled about Helios and brings them without confusion into unity with Helios, the King of the All: and she distributes and is the channel for stainless and pure life throughout the seven spheres, from the highest vault of the heavens as far as Selene the Moon: for Selene is the last of the heavenly spheres which Athene fills with wisdom: and by her aid Selene beholds the intelligible which is higher than the heavens, and adorns with its forms the realm of matter that lies below her, and thus she does away with its savagery and confusion and disorder. Moreover to mankind Athene gives the blessings of wisdom and intelligence and the creative arts. And surely she dwells in the capitols of cities because, through her wisdom, she has established the community of the state. I have still to say a few words about Aphrodite, who, as the wise men among the Phoenicians affirm, and as I believe, assists Helios in his creative function. She is, in very truth, a synthesis of the heavenly gods, and in their harmony she is the spirit of love and unity. For she[1] is very near to Helios, and when she pursues the same course as he and approaches him, she fills the skies with fair weather and gives generative power to the earth: for she herself takes thought for the continuous birth of living things. And though of that continuous birth King Helios is the primary creative cause, yet Aphrodite is the joint cause with him, she who enchants our souls with her charm and sends down to earth from the upper air rays of light most sweet and stainless, aye, more lustrous than gold itself.

Again, does he not set in motion the whole of nature and kindle life therein, by bestowing on it generative power from on high? But for the divided natures also, is not he the cause that they journey to their appointed end?[2] For Aristotle says that man is begotten by man and the sun together. Accordingly the same theory about King Helios must surely apply to all the other activities of the divided souls. Again, does he not produce for us rain and wind and the clouds in the skies, by employing, as though it were matter, the two kinds of vapour? For when he heats the earth he draws up steam and smoke, and from these there arise not only the clouds but also all the physical changes on our earth, both great and small.

But why do I deal with the same questions at such length, when I am free at last to come to my goal, though not till I have first celebrated all the blessings that Helios has given to mankind? For from him are we born, and by him are we nourished. But his more divine gifts, and all that he bestows on our souls when he frees them from the body and then lifts them up on high to the region of those substances that are akin to the god; and the fineness and vigour of his divine rays, which are assigned as a sort of vehicle for the safe descent of our souls into

[1] As the planet Venus.   [2] The ascent after death of human souls to the gods.

this world of generation; all this, I say, let others celebrate in
fitting strains, but let me believe it rather than demonstrate its
truth. However, I need not hesitate to discuss so much as is
known to all. Plato says that the sky is our instructor in wisdom.
For from its contemplation we have learned to know the
nature of number, whose distinguishing characteristics we know
only from the course of the sun. Plato himself says that day and
night were created first. And next, from observing the moon's
light, which was bestowed on the goddess by Helios, we later
progressed still further in the understanding of these matters:
in every case conjecturing the harmony of all things with this
god. For Plato himself says somewhere that our race was by
nature doomed to toil, and so the gods pitied us and gave us
Dionysus and the Muses as playfellows. And we recognized that
Helios is their common lord, since he is celebrated as the father
of Dionysus and the leader of the Muses. And has not Apollo,
who is his colleague in empire, set up oracles in every part of
the earth, and given to men inspired wisdom, and regulated
their cities by means of religious and political ordinances? And
he has civilized the greater part of the world by means of Greek
colonies, and so made it easier for the world to be governed by
the Romans. For the Romans themselves not only belong to
the Greek race, but also the sacred ordinances and the pious
belief in the gods which they have established and maintain are,
from beginning to end, Greek. And beside this they have established a constitution not inferior to that of any one of the best-
governed states, if indeed it be not superior to all others that
have ever been put into practice. For which reason I myself
recognize that our city is Greek, both in descent and as to its
constitution.

Shall I now go on to tell you how Helios took thought for
the health and safety of all men by begetting Asclepios[1] to be

[1] Asclepios plays an important part in Julian's religion, and may have been
intentionally opposed, as the son of Helios-Mithras and the 'saviour of the
world', to Jesus Christ.

the saviour of the whole world? And how he bestowed on us every kind of excellence by sending down to us Aphrodite together with Athene, and thus laid down for our protection what is almost a law, that we should only unite to beget our kind? Surely it is for this reason that, in agreement with the course of the sun, all plants and all the tribes of living things are aroused to bring forth their kind. What need is there for me to glorify his beams and his light? For surely everyone knows how terrible is night without a moon or stars, so that from this he can calculate how great a boon for us is the light of the sun? And this very light he supplies at night, without ceasing, and directly, from the moon in those upper spaces where it is needed, while he grants us through the night a truce from toil. But there would be no limit to the account if one should endeavour to describe all his gifts of this sort. For there is no single blessing in our lives which we do not receive as a gift from this god, either perfect from him alone, or, through the other gods, perfected by him.

Moreover he is the founder of our city. For not only does Zeus, who is glorified as the father of all things, inhabit its citadel together with Athene and Aphrodite, but Apollo also dwells on the Palatine Hill, and Helios himself under this name of his which is commonly known to all and familiar to all.

In Rome maiden priestesses guard the undying flame of the sun at different hours in turn; they guard the fire that is produced on earth by the agency of the god. And I can tell you a still greater proof of the power of this god, which is the work of that most divine king himself. The months are reckoned from the moon by, one may say, all other peoples; but we and the Egyptians alone reckon the days of every year according to the movements of the sun. If after this I should say that we also worship Mithras, and celebrate games in honour of Helios every four years, I shall be speaking of customs that are somewhat recent. But perhaps it is better to cite a proof from the remote past. The beginning of the cycle of the year is placed at different times by different peoples. Some place it at the spring equinox, others at the height of summer, and many in the late autumn; but they each and all sing the praises of the most visible gifts of Helios. One nation celebrates the season best adapted for work in the fields, when the earth bursts into bloom and exults, when all the crops are just beginning to sprout, and the sea begins to be safe for sailing, and the disagreeable, gloomy winter puts on a more cheerful aspect; others again award the crown to the summer season, since at that time they can safely feel confidence about the yield of the fruits, when the grains have already been harvested and midsummer is now at its height, and the fruits on the trees are ripening. Others again, with still more subtlety, regard as the close of the year the time when all the fruits are in their perfect prime and decay has already set in. For this reason they celebrate the annual festival of the New Year in late autumn. But our forefathers, from the time of the most divine king Numa, paid still greater reverence to the god Helios. They ignored the question of mere utility, I think, because they were naturally religious and endowed with unusual intelligence; but they saw that he is the cause of all that is useful, and so they ordered the observance of the New Year to correspond with the present season; that is to say when King Helios returns to us again, and leaving the region furthest south and, rounding Capricorn as though it were a goal-post, advances from the south to the north to give us our share of the blessings of the year. And that our forefathers, because they comprehended this correctly, thus established the beginning of the year, one may perceive from the following. For it was not, I think, the time when the god turns, but the time when he becomes visible to all men, as he travels from south to north, that they appointed for the festival. For still unknown to them was the nicety of those laws which the Chaldeans and Egyptians discovered, and which Hipparchus and Ptolemy perfected: but they judged simply by sense-perception, and were limited to what they could actually see.

But the truth of these facts was recognized, as I said, by a later generation. Before the beginning of the year, at the end of the month which is called after Kronos, we celebrate in honour of Helios the most splendid games, and we dedicate the festival to the Invincible Sun. And after this it is not lawful to perform any of the shows that belong to the last month, gloomy as they are, though necessary. But, in the cycle, immediately after the end of the Kronia[1] follow the Heliaia. That festival may the ruling gods grant me to praise and to celebrate with sacrifice! And above all the others may Helios himself, the King of the All, grant me this, even he who from eternity has proceeded from the generative substance of the Good: even he who is midmost of the midmost intellectual gods; who fills them with continuity and endless beauty and reason, yea with all blessings at once, and independently of time! And now he illumines his own visible abode, which from eternity moves as the centre of the whole heavens, and bestows a share of intelligible beauty on the whole visible world, and fills the whole heavens with the same number of gods as he contains in himself in intellectual form. And without division they reveal themselves in manifold form surrounding him, but they are attached to him to form a unity. Aye, but also, through his perpetual generation and the blessings that he bestows from the heavenly bodies, he holds together the region beneath the moon. For he cares for the whole human race in common, but especially for my own city, even as also he brought into being my soul from eternity, and made it his follower. All this, therefore, that I prayed for a moment ago, may he grant, and further may he, of his grace, endow my city as a whole with eternal existence, so far as is possible, and protect her; and for myself personally, may he grant that, so long

---

[1] Another name for the festival of Saturn, the Saturnalia, celebrated by the Latins at the close of December.

as I am permitted to live, I may prosper in my affairs both human and divine; finally may he grant me to live and serve the state with my life, so long as is pleasing to himself and well for me and expedient for the Roman Empire!

This discourse, friend Sallust, I composed in three nights at most, in harmony with the threefold creative power of the god,[1] as far as possible just as it occurred to my memory.

Since I wished to compose a hymn to express my gratitude to the god, I thought that this was the best place in which to tell, to the best of my power, of his essential nature. And so I think that not in vain has this discourse been composed. For the saying 'To the extent of your powers offer sacrifice to the immortal gods', I apply not to sacrifice only, but also to the praises that we offer to the gods. For the third time, therefore, I pray that Helios, the King of the All, may be gracious to me in recompense for this my zeal; and may he grant me a virtuous life and more perfect wisdom and inspired intelligence, and, when fate wills, the gentlest exit that may be from life, at a fitting hour; and that I may ascend to him thereafter and abide with him, for ever if possible, but if that be more than the actions of my life deserve, for many periods of many years!

[1] Julian means that there are three modes of creation exercised by Helios now in one, now in another, of the three worlds.

INDEX

267